CARBINE

The Story of
David Marshall Williams

Photo by Jim Wommack

Carbine

The Story of David Marshall Williams

Ross E. Beard, Jr.

Photographs by Richard Dunlap

PHILLIPS PUBLICATIONS, WILLIAMSTOWN, NJ 08094

A large portion of the
Carbine Williams Weapons Collection
is now located in the
South Carolina Military History Museum,
Columbia, South Carolina.

This book is only available from the South Carolina Military Museum (address below) at a cost of $24.00 including shipping and handling.

FIRST EDITION
Hard Cover
© 1977 by Ross E. Beard, Jr.

SECOND EDITION
Hard Cover
© 1997 by Ross E. Beard, Jr.

THIRD EDITION
Soft Cover
© 2007 Ross E. Beard, Jr.

Published by:
HONORIBUS PRESS
P.O. Box 4872
Spartanburg, SC 29305

South Carolina Military Museum
1225 Bluff Road
Columbia, SC 29201
Phone (803) 806-4440
Fax (803) 806-2103

International Standard Book Number: 1-885354-26-6

Printed in the United States of America
ALTMAN PRINTING CO., INC.
Spartanburg, South Carolina

TO

"Miss Maggie"
(Mrs. David Marshall Williams)

and

Martha Hansard Roach

*Without these two special people this book
would not have been completed.*

Table of Contents

List of Illustrations

BLANK PAGE

Foreword

As I have grown older, I have become more and more convinced that America's greatness is not the result of one's education or one's wealth, nor is our greatness the result of giant corporations' desire to make money. Our greatness and our strength come from the thoughts, dreams, ideas and the drive and determination of strong individuals that are in all walks of American life and woven into the fabric of our country.

David Marshall Williams ("Carbine" Williams) was most certainly one of these unique and dynamic individuals and I am honored to have met him, to have worked with him, and to have earned his friendship. For more than 12 years I spent my weekends at his shop, in his home, walking the fields with him, shooting, getting to know his wonderful family and during this time earning his trust. Earning his trust was not easy. He had been taken advantage of many times and was a man of many moods. During my visits I sometimes experienced his verbal and physical assaults, but I was obsessed with getting to know this remarkable man better. During these years, I watched as he formulated an idea in his mind, created and actually made new and remarkable weapons. Many are still ahead of their time today. Above all else, I discovered a man with a big heart behind that rough exterior, a man that cared about his family and country.

We had exact rules. I had to arrive at his shop at 7:00 AM and over the 12 years we never sat down in his shop. We stood and talked until noon. Then, the highlight of my day was a return to his house where his wife, whom I lovingly called "Miss Maggie," prepared a wonderful meal and even more wonderful tea and dessert. "Carbine" always gave the blessing which included "Blessing all the ships at sea!" We would then return to the shop and resume our standing and talking and examination of guns or shooting out of the shop window (one of my favorite pastimes).

Over the years, as "Carbine" expanded his trust in me, he slowly and deliberately poured out to me thousands of previously uncommunicated facts about all phases of extraordinary life. Eventually I introduced him to a tape recorder and it took a lot of "getting used to," but we recorded hundreds of daylong interviews in the form of conversations derived from questions I would think of during the week and ask during my visit. I also spent countless hours going over old newspapers, articles, court records, patents and other documents containing facts about this man. I wrote publishers, to the patent office and many other sources in government seeking information about "Carbine." Most were very cooperative and while many were a bit awed by this man, all respected him. There were a few that were quite jealous of him too!

I found that "Carbine" wanted his story told correctly, honestly, and in total and he was very honest and straightforward with me. Once in a while I would feel the necessity of "checking" out some facts or information and in one such incident I just didn't bother to tell "Carbine" that I intended to spend a full day in the courthouse reviewing his trial records. After a long wait, a young lady "found" the records and worked with me all day, helping in every way to provide what I needed. At the end of the day I suggested she let me pay her for all her help. She refused very graciously, but said, "You can do me a favor if you will. . . ." I readily agreed and she said, "When you get back to Uncle Marsh's shop, please tell him I said hello!" She was "Carbine's" niece and had called to confirm that she should "find" these records and assist me! On my arrival at the shop "Carbine" was standing in the door and with a grin said, "I understand you have been real busy today, REB. . . ." (I was thankful he was in a good mood!)

Until now the real and full story of this man had never been told purely and simply because he did not want it told. Many "assumed" a lot of things, but few had access to him for 12 long years. Interestingly enough, his family had never discussed the many events in "Carbine's" life and, at his death, I was privileged to sit at the table with the entire family and we started an "exchange" of memories. . . . To my astonishment as one would remember or comment on some point in his life, the others would say, "I didn't know that!" Hundreds of facts were added to my book at that point and I feel it was good for the family to have had this exchange of memories. In the matter-of-fact manner of these wonderful people, Gordon, "Carbine's" brother, said, "Until now, we had no reason to discuss this." "Carbine's" inventions revolutionized weaponry in America and around the world. Many innovations and improvements to weapons came from thoughts and ideas that he had in his mind while confined in "the box" (solitary confinement) in prison. Long after his .30 cal. carbine became "obsolete," military men often threw down the later military models and found and used this little weapon.

On really getting to know David Marshall Williams, I was driven to write his biography. I am thankful I could complete this book and record for history the name of David M. "Carbine" Williams along with those of Colt and Browning when listing the few inventive geniuses in the field of American weapons' development.

I pray that this book will serve in some small way to recognize the numerous important contributions made by this weapons' genius to both the defenses of our country and to the hunting and shooting pleasures of us gun lovers throughout the world.

Ross E. Beard, Jr.
Camden, SC

CHAPTER 1
The First Visit

After discovering through a twist of fate that the colorful and famous weapons inventor David Marshall "Carbine" Williams lived near Godwin, North Carolina, I was filled with an overwhelming desire to meet this man personally. I immediately sat down and with my two-finger typing dashed off a letter addressed to the inventor at Route 1, Godwin. I hoped he would eventually receive the letter though it was sent to an unconfirmed address. In the corner of my envelope I typed the following return address: REB, 1821 Forest Drive, Camden, South Carolina. Later I learned that my return address was the key that opened the door to meeting David M. Williams and resulted in our developing a long-term and strong friendship.

In about ten days I was excited to find in my mailbox a letter boldly addressed to REB Beard, and in the upper lefthand corner was the return address: David M. "Carbine" Williams, Godwin, North Carolina. I had difficulty opening this letter carefully, but as a collector, I knew that I should preserve the envelope. On initial examination of the envelope I sensed an orderliness. The address was carefully centered, and the stamp placed precisely equidistant from the top and righthand end of the envelope. As eagerly as possible I opened this letter and my heart pounded as I read Carbine Williams' invitation to visit his shop in Godwin. I had mentioned in my letter that I owned a .30 caliber carbine which, unfortunately, was inoperable. Williams suggested that I bring the rifle along. "I 'might' be able to fix it for you," he wrote.

I discussed the trip with my wife, Anne, and it was settled that we would drive to Godwin the following Saturday for a visit. A letter advising Carbine and his wife of our acceptance of his invitation was mailed and nine o'clock was established as the time of arrival.

Following a three-hour drive on the appointed day, we arrived in Godwin, a crossroads marked with several decrepit buildings and a faded town limits sign. Finding only one store open, we asked directions to Carbine's home. The store owner, obviously a friend of Williams and not too trusting of dressed-up strangers, pointedly asked, "Why do you want to know?" I produced Carbine's letter of invitation, whereupon his attitude changed abruptly. Quite cordially he directed us two miles farther down old U.S. 301 highway. We were cautioned that there was no identification of Carbine Williams on the mailbox, but that his brother Shell's mailbox marked the turning point for entering Carbine's property.

As we approached the inventor's homesite, we were charmed with the little white, weatherboarded house, far back from the road, beautifully maintained, with many flowers and plants surrounding it. We parked on the grass beside the house and hurriedly went up to the front door, excited at the thought of meeting this legendary inventor. (This was the first and only time I ever went in the front door, for friends of the Williamses enter through the back porch, I was to learn.)

As we stepped upon the porch, a tiny, smiling and most gracious lady stepped out to greet us. "Miss Maggie," Carbine's wife, welcomed us and told us how pleased she was that we had come to visit. "I must tell you," she warned, "that 'Marsh' (short for his first name — Marshall) drinks. He has not had visitors in a long time and has become quite excited about your visit. He has been drinking recently but I think he's all right today." She further explained that Marsh had not made a habit of either opening, reading or answering letters in recent years, but he was fascinated with my "REB" return address. Wanting to know who had the initials REB, he had opened my letter and subsequently invited us up for this visit. Finding that he had been drinking did not upset me at the time. I was flattered that his invitation was such a special one and I eagerly entered the home to meet him.

As we stood in the living room of this pleasant home, Miss Maggie called out, "Marsh, Mr. and Mrs. Beard are here." I paused here to note that I had a mental picture of this famous inventor, for I had seen one photograph of him that was made in the early 1950s—a strong, red-haired, determined and ruggedly handsome man. In a minute or two, there appeared in the doorway leading to the dining room one hell of a man: sideburns down to the corners of his mouth, hair quite tousled, the most fierce blue eyes I have ever seen—a man attired in bib overalls, high-top shoes, and with not one, but two, .45 caliber automatics, barrels up, protruding ominously from his hip pockets.

Moving with sort of a side gait, yet very direct, the inventor entered the room, extended his hand and, when grasping mine, crunched my gold ring against my finger so tightly that I had to have the ring cut off the next day by a jeweler. His first words of greeting were, "So you're REB. Boy, I hope I'm a gonna like you." As I grimaced under the pressure of his grip and as I looked at this fierce man and those two .45 automatics, I offered a mental prayer, "God knows, I hope he likes me too."

Following the initial greeting, we were seated in the living room and Carbine began to ask me exactly what I knew about him. I had never felt so totally inadequate or uninformed. At the time I had no idea that Williams had invented weapons other than the .30 caliber carbine. I was to find out as our friendship grew that this man held fifty-nine major patents in the field of firearms. And that, unlike any other inventor in the history of America, he had not only come up with the idea, but designed, hand made, perfected and delivered the finished product to each particular company concerned. He had been an inventor for Remington, Winchester and Colt, and had performed development work for the Ordnance Department, which is responsible for weapons development for all of the U.S. military services. I was further amazed to find that he delayed patenting one invention, a self-setting trigger, for a long time, "because I didn't know how to explain how the damn thing worked—you see, I know what I want a thing to do and I just flat make it do it." An inventor he was; a technical writer he was not.

Carbine Williams has always had a reputation for having an eye for the ladies, and my wife was quite beautiful. Time and again, Williams would "prison whisper" (whisper without moving his lips) to me: "Ross, you can tell me, boy, is this really your wife or is she a girl friend?" I repeatedly confirmed and insisted that Anne was indeed my wife, but somehow, at that time, Carbine could not quite fit us together. Frankly, I imagined he felt that an ugly mutt like me could not have had such a beautiful woman for a wife, or even a girl friend for that matter. Our relationship was finally established, however, and while often strong and tough with me, Marshall Williams always had a very special and very warm smile for Anne, and always extended every courtesy and consideration to her.

I was so excited and under such stress during this visit that I completely forgot about the inoperative carbine in the trunk of my car. But Carbine remembered and invited me to bring it in so he could examine it. I did, and with the deft hand of an inventor, and utilizing his huge magnifying glass (Photo 1), he stripped the piece and in seconds smiled knowingly. "Ross, leave her with me," he suggested. "I'll doctor her up, and you can pick her up on your next trip to Godwin." I registered double excitement at this point: I would have a carbine actually repaired and zeroed in by the inventor; further, he had agreed to autograph it for me. But most important was his invitation to return for another visit.

At no time during the first visit was Williams' shop mentioned or discussed, nor was a single weapon men-

Photo 1. Always at hand was this magnifying glass with which Carbine carefully examined gun parts he had made. He needed no such glass when shooting, however. "I'll shoot my birds and yours, REB, if you ain't fast," he promised.

tioned (other than my own and the two .45s displayed in his pocket). For him, this visit was obviously one of getting to know a stranger, one where a sizing up took place. I was to learn later the reason for this: In earlier days many visitors to Carbine Williams' residence had abused the privilege of being there.

As this first visit ended, Anne and I began to bid farewell to Carbine and Miss Maggie, and then and there a little ritual was established. While we would usually say good-bye to Miss Maggie at the back door of the back porch, Carbine would walk us out to the car. We would very solemnly shake hands. I would be instructed to drive carefully and to keep my arm inside the car, not hanging out the window. And as I would leave his farm, drive out to the dirt road and turn left on U.S. 301, I would signal with the horn, and from across the field I would see Marshall Williams standing by the gate to his house, his huge Stetson hat in hand, waving a warm farewell to us.

We visited again and again, and our friendship grew. As time progressed, I decided that it would be a very practical thing to bring a tape recorder with me. During the years of visiting Carbine, I placed a tape recorder in his shop and taped him in jovial moods and moments of sadness, in deep discussion, in displays of boisterous profanity. During these visits I shot with Carbine Williams, I sat at his table, I heard his prayer, became acquainted with his family and, in my opinion, I was a privileged young man.

CHAPTER 2
Inventor Meets Photographer

It was not long before I decided that I should take with me to Godwin a very qualified and outstanding photographer to photograph Carbine Williams at work in an authentic setting. But much more came about than just the photographs: I was able to witness another's reaction upon his initial meeting with Carbine Williams.

Photographer Richard Dunlap relates in his own words the events which took place during his first visit to Godwin.

Ross Beard and I agreed that in compiling the facts necessary to construct a biography of Carbine Williams it would be absolutely necessary to know this man intimately. Heretofore, his story had been told largely in short magazine articles which mainly covered the weapons aspect of his life, along with incidental superficial impressions of those writers who had met and interviewed him. Their erroneous summation was, for the most part, that this good-time plowboy from the backwoods had accidentally stumbled across a few good ideas for guns and that the timing just happened to coincide with the Great War. And so, almost overnight, he had become a wizard in the world of gun designing. Nothing could have been further from the truth.

The one serious attempt at telling the Carbine Williams story to a wide audience was the 1952 movie *Carbine Williams,* which received top billing when actor

Jimmy Stewart played the lead role. But it too had its limitations and was necessarily incomplete. In certain places it was inaccurate.

When we first met Carbine it had been two years since he had been interviewed for a story, a lengthy work, incidentally, which was published in a gun magazine early in 1964, nearly two years after the interview took place. To obtain the inventor's cooperation, and to insure a complete and accurate record of the events of his life, we knew that it was necessary to convince the man of our sincerity and to obtain his trust and blessing. In fact, the entire Williams family must be convinced that another round of notoriety was not in the making.

Dealing with Carbine was difficult. Not that he would not cooperate—he did. However, the following chronology of events during my first visit to Godwin will provide some indication of how Carbine Williams reacts to outsiders, and how they, in turn, react to Carbine.

Few people, even his old friends and neighbors, had close ties with Carbine at the time of our meeting. During his sixty-fourth year, he had reached the point where, as he put it, "It's awright if people like you, but it ain't absolutely necessary." A decade can make a great difference in a man; especially, it had with this one. Ten years earlier he had been an important celebrity, the toast of Hollywood for a period of a year or more. But this success took him for the proverbial "ride" and he reputedly spent more money in living high on the West Coast than he made on the film concerning his life. The aftermath of that experience might have left him on the defensive, but to use that expression in his presence would have invited physical abuse.

And I mean physical abuse. When you visited Carbine Williams in those days you had better keep your mouth shut and your hands in your pockets, at least that first visit. He at one time had been easier to get along with, although even then he was described as a playful Saint Bernard. He would sock you in the chest or pull a draw on you with his gold-gripped .45 just to see how you would take it.

Even in the 1960s he remained playful—if you were his friend—but he continued to be suspicious of people and their motives. He had threatened "to cut this thing out of seeing people." So now the only way to get to the heart of Carbine was to demonstrate friendliness—and this required extreme diplomacy and tact.

The first time I took a tape recorder and camera into his shop I was amazed at how easily he took to them. It was evident that he had had his photograph taken many times and had been interviewed for radio and television and the like. He took to it naturally because there was a certain vanity about him. It was not braggadocio—it was just that he had been the center of attraction all those years, and now in the twilight of his life, he revelled in directing every aspect of a discussion.

Mean? No, he was not mean. But I believe that if anyone had ever made the mistake of intentionally insulting him, he might have just shot him. He had a loaded gun at his fingertips every moment of his life—a .45 automatic with zinc bullets. Potentially, a very classy way to go, if you like to look at it that way.

Ross Beard, who had visited Carbine several times before, had briefed me before my first visit on what to do (very little, he stressed) and what not to do (a considerably more extensive list). We were supposed to arrive at Godwin a little after nine on a Saturday morning, but car trouble caused a delay and it was 11:15 before we rolled into Carbine's yard.

Williams was standing in the backyard, obviously ill-at-ease about the delay. He was dressed up in his Sunday best for the pictures, complete with a white shirt, double-breasted blue pinstriped suit, off-white Stetson hat, fancy suspenders, wide belt with an engraved golden western buckle, and a cross-draw holster filled with that ornate .45.

He welcomed us cordially, eyes sparkling, and his handshake proved less crippling by my forethought in removing the ring from my right hand. I immediately felt relieved because he smiled, and because his wife, Maggie, was a picture of the Southern hostess, inquiring of our wants—coffee, iced tea, and so forth.

From early published pictures of him, you could see that Carbine had been a dashing man during his day. He carried this manner into his early fifties. Rugged to begin with, he had better-than-average good looks. With acting ability, it is not unlikely that he could have been a success playing himself in his own motion picture. He was not without playboy characteristics. During his prime inventive years he was rich, and although he did not worship money he knew how to spend it, and God knows he did. Williams had been red-haired then and packed spike-bending power into his five-foot, nine-inch frame, which showed that he had carried a big work burden in his day. Ruddy, but light complexioned, he weighed perhaps one hundred and eighty pounds.

Meeting Williams in the mid-sixties, you could see how the past decade had taken its toll. He had suffered a serious stroke which climaxed a period of physical and mental punishment. His hair was no longer red but mixed with gray. He was bent noticeably but moved with determination-straight ahead always. His complexion remained fair and his sideburns had lengthened, extending to and flaring widely at his cheeks. This more than anything else gave him a distinction and added to his overall rugged appearance. His blue eyes now appeared reddish and moist, but remained capable of rendering a domineering stare. He showed no indication of baldness; in fact his hair, with benefit of a tint, would have done justice to a young man.

Carbine seldom smiled, yet was capable of a hearty laugh among friends. He loved to reminisce, and when he talked of his mother or his wife in melancholy tones, he at times shed a tear or two. He was reverent to God, but could cause the air to blister with vile epithets. He talked easily about most things, but there were a few subjects that were sacred. "Don't push me," he would warn, with a prolonged stare that could make your blood run cold.

Yes, I suppose if you had run into him on the street, you might have taken him for a harmless old man. But I would have welcomed him any day as a partner in a barroom brawl.

Williams' moods changed quickly. He had a sharp sense of humor, and he loved to demonstrate it. He could talk about music, recite poetry, be witty. He was amazingly descriptive, and you could miss a great deal of this if you were not alert every moment when he was talking. We found this in our recordings. He used the vernacular of his youth, and sometimes you had to try to decipher what he meant by a word or a phrase.

Modern life had no appeal for him. He perferred to live with the past. He still wore a double-breasted suit, wide tie and high-top shoes with hooks. His home had a radio but no television, and he seemed somewhat disinterested in the subjects of our space age; yet, he kept up with those things technical and otherwise which were important to him.

It was easy to see that Carbine suffered from his past. He said he had no regrets—certainly he would not admit them—but there were scars on his heart, and they festered at times to make him suffer. He was a sentimentalist and therefore took life earnestly. You felt yourself being concerned for this man who had given so much of himself but who could not face his last years at peace with himself.

What troubled him? Probably four things, primarily: his guilt over his years of separation from Maggie; his son, and the fact that there was so much distance between them in miles, and possibly in understanding; an $80,000 income tax debt to the government; and the broken dreams he was forced to face as the result of losing his fortune.

While we were unloading our camera and recorder equipment from the car during my first visit, Carbine flagged me in the yard and inquired, "You boys bring along a little bottle?" Although we had not planned it that way, we felt a little guilty to report that we hadn't indeed. He then hinted broadly that it might be a good idea to get into the town of Dunn before noon because he thought many of the state beverage stores would close at that hour.

What could we say? We frankly were afraid to protest since we were not at all sure how he would respond to this. More importantly, we did not know how he would react to a No. An excuse was made that we had to go into town for some extra recording batteries, and Ross departed for Dunn, leaving me alone to make peace with this Tiger of Cumberland County.

Carbine looked on as I set up the tape, and during the next half hour we recorded some very important material from radio interview records Carbine had made in Asheville when his picture opened there, and from the Twentieth Century Limited train interview in New York before his departure for Hollywood.

An amusing incident then took place, one that may have been the opening for a more relaxed association between Carbine Williams and me. Carbine was standing in the kitchen with Mrs. Williams and me when she left the room to get some old photographs which we had asked to copy.

Carbine immediately lunged for the cabinet under the sink and, after fumbling around with his hand while looking out for Miss Maggie with one eye, fished out an Irish potato from a bag and slipped it into his coat pocket. He looked at me and smiled as if he had pulled a fast one on me as well as on Miss Maggie.

Mrs. Williams didn't return for a minute so I smiled back at him and said, "I know that old trick, too!" He looked at me disbelievingly and I went on to explain, "You see, to take a bite out of that potato is the best way known to kill the scent of whiskey on the breath." It's not widely known as a breath freshener, but as fate would have it I had run across this information only a month before. It happened that a friend of mine, Jake Penland, sports editor of *The State* newspaper in Columbia, South Carolina, had told me about it. Jake had heard it from an old-timer on a bus trip from Atlanta when he was returning from a football game, and had passed this little gem on to me.

So by this coincidence I was prepared for Carbine's little deception. If Mrs. Williams didn't know about it by then, I'm sure she had been wondering where all her potatoes had been disappearing to all those years.

It was noon before Ross returned with some "extra" batteries for our portable tape recorder. (He had taken them out of the set before he returned.) We put our heads together and agreed that we would head over to Carbine's work building to begin taking pictures and making tapes. Mrs. Williams informed us that lunch would be ready at one o'clock, so we didn't have much time to work before then. We piled into the car and rode to the shop, located some three hundred yards across a field punctuated by a grove of mulberry trees. There were three roads leading to the shop.

We parked the car a few yards from the building and walked toward the only door leading into it. The little building was neat and, unlike the other two nearby, was painted white with green double doors on the front and green-trimmed windows. It measured about fifteen by twenty-five feet. There was no shrubbery around it — nothing within thirty yards but cleared ground. A grape arbor grew at the rear; a mulberry grove stood to the east, flanked by a dark log cabin; an old well pump was located to the south; and another house (the smokehouse), where the famous models were kept, was to the west.

As we entered the workshop I became aware of another thing. Carbine at sixty-four, didn't need or want any assistance. The natural thing for a young man to do is to be considerate and let a more elderly man go first. Not the case with Carbine. No one walked behind him. He insisted on bringing up the rear.

And you couldn't touch him! Other than a handshake, he preferred no physical contact — under any circumstances. I tried to help him up the steps to his workshop by taking an elbow, only to receive it in the ribs.

We stepped into his workshop and entered a new world. It resembled a man's private den in a way with numerous mementos and guns on the walls. Once we grew accustomed to the layout it appeared to have clearly defined sections to it, although there were no closed-off areas. As you entered the door there was a large milling machine in the middle of the floor; in the right rear corner a lathe ran along the wall; and in the center of the room a homely little pot-bellied stove gave off a glow and heated the place comfortably (Photo 2). There were three windows on each side of the building, two in the front and two in the back. They extended from the top of his work benches nearly to the ceiling, letting in both the early morning and late afternoon light. We took many pictures in this room without flash and found that all received adequate exposure.

One side of the room contained all of Williams' gleaming, handmade tools — precisely in their proper places. There was about a five-foot space on the west wall where he kept many of his duplicate guns, but these were not the ones he valued. Also in his shop were many mementos — swords, old pistols, rifles, shotguns, daggers, parts of machine guns, a bull whip, an old Stetson hat that he had probably worn out, pictures of his family, certificates of honorary memberships, specifications charts, old prints, a bear trap which belonged to his great-grandfather, a bugle, samples of all types of ordnance shells, a tomahawk, fox horns, a license plate from Connecticut with only his initials on it, a buffalo and deer head, and finally, a Confederate flag and an engraving of General Robert E. Lee. "I'm a Robert E. Lee man and proud of it," Carbine drawled sincerely.

I was nervous at the beginning and, frankly, I think he was a little on edge, too. He was expecting us to begin the photography and taping immediately. We fumbled with the tape and, with his help, rigged it up on a stool and plugged the power cord into a light socket in the middle of the room. We looped the microphone over the top of the drive belt on his milling machine and turned it on.

Carbine cut loose with abandon, touching all bases in the first few minutes, asking what we wanted to talk about, and spicing the narrative with solid punches to our

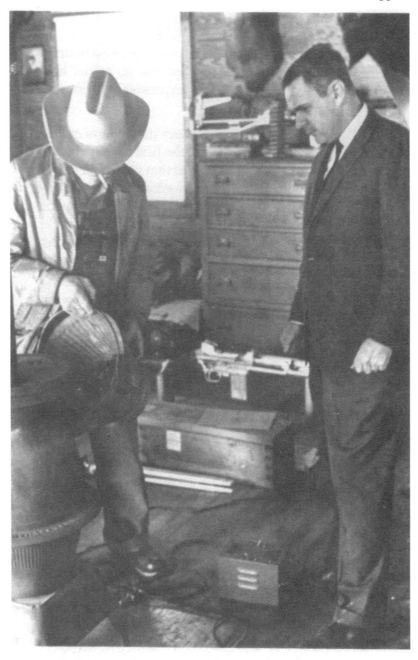

Photo 2. The morning ritual included stoking the pot-bellied stove before starting the day's work. Williams realized the consequences of temperature change when working with metals.

chests. We stood with hands in pockets or with arms folded, taking it all, for we realized that no matter how intimidating he was to us, we were experiencing an integral part of Carbine's personality.

The morning's taping put about three hours of livid description in our tape file. After the first hour had raced by, we suddenly became concerned that we would be late for Mrs. Williams' lunch, which we knew was ready by then. But we had one hell of a time getting Carbine to wind up the recording session. Ross had noticeably glanced at his watch several times when Carbine abruptly announced: "I don't like people looking at their watch!"

Finally we were able to adjourn and arrived back at his home twenty minutes late for lunch. I felt like an apology was in order and considered shifting the blame to the man responsible; however, I thought better of that. Besides, Mrs. William didn't seem to mind our tardiness.

Once inside the neat little cottage, we noticed a decided change in the personality of the inventor. He became softer, and it was obvious that it was out of sincere regard for his Maggie. You could sense he was proud or her and, though he was still man of the house, he wished for her the opportunity to become hostess for the guests. It was a pleasant sensation to come from the shop into the quietness of her home — like getting in out of a storm, to be honest. We more than welcomed this phase of the visit, for we soon realized that Mrs. Williams had always played a significant role in Carbine's life. We knew by her manner that she would be invaluable in filling in the fine details which were so necessary in relating her husband's complete story.

We were ushered into a charming dining room and were seated before a tastefully decorated walnut table set with Mrs. Williams' best china and sterling tableware. A white linen tablecloth and a flower arrangement completed the setting. From the head of the table Carbine faced Miss Maggie, with Ross on his left and I on his right.

"Would you like to say grace, Daddy?" Mrs. Williams asked. We both learned that this was a carry-over from the days when they were raising their only son, David, by that time married and living in California.

"Should I say the long one?" he asked. Without a reply, we bowed our heads and Carbine began a quick, simple, scarcely audible prayer. He asked for protection of our men at sea, made a plea for his son, and then allowed a brief pause at the end for others present to conduct their private communication with God. Carbine then raised his head and smiled, and we began to serve: Waldorf salad, baked chicken, sweet potatoes, snap beans seasoned with bacon, fresh creamy sweet corn, coffee and, finally, pecan pie. We talked of making good desserts, mockingbirds, life on the old plantations and quail hunting. The interlude passed quickly; we knew that it would be a busy afternoon.

Carbine had transported many of his important weapons from his smokehouse to the workshop so that we might photograph them. We began doing this as he held each and described some of the circumstances of its manufacture.

Progress was fast and productive until we reached the .22 caliber machine gun, which contributed another high point for the day. We agreed that we would take the gun outside for this picture, so I went out to search for a proper spot; Carbine and Ross carried out the tripod and the gun and set it up on the ground.

As we were about to take the photograph it occurred to Carbine that he didn't have a cartridge belt in the gun, so he returned to the shop to get one. As he came out the door, it also occurred to him that this might be an opportune time to demonstrate how some prisoners he had known made a break by garroting the guards. He charged toward me as I knelt there with a camera strap already around my neck.

I could see it coming, but in that split second I had no time to consider just how realistic he intended to be. I allowed him to place the first loop of the belt around my neck, but when it tightened down hard, I clutched for it. The second loop went around, but I got a couple of fingers under it and it was diverted between the teeth. Carbine tightened down forcefully and I was jerked back on my rump. Ross yelled Whoa! and Carbine eased off. He stood there looking at me, smiling broadly, obviously pleased with my expression. (I carried a red whelp on my neck for several days, and as a trophy of the day I possess a white shirt with a collar striped with cosmoline grease.)

I figured the worst was over with this episode and we could finish out the day in a more relaxed, friendly atmosphere. Wrong!

We had stood up all these hours in the shop because Carbine almost never sat down. He liked to stand while talking, especially when he was in his own working surroundings. Therefore, everybody else stood up, too.

It was by then about four-thirty in the afternoon, and I knew that, despite the relatively short time we had been there, it had been tough work and Carbine was probably getting a little tired of fooling with us.

The subject of machine guns came up again and he asked Ross if he wanted to run through a belt of .30 calibers before we left. Now Ross is an ardent gun collector himself, but government rules about machine guns being what they are, he doesn't have the opportunity to shoot them too often. So, naturally, he thought this suggestion was a splendid one.

They hauled a .30 caliber machine gun into the yard. They had a little trouble getting the gun mounted in the tripod, so Carbine took over and directed a sawhorse be set up. He would fire the first burst from it freehand, without tripod, to get it started for Ross.

I knelt down some ten yards away to get a picture. My Rolli-flex camera around my neck, I peered down into it in preparation for snapping the picture just as they cut loose with the first burst.

But the first burst I didn't photograph. What I saw through the lens was the gun going off and Carbine being backed away from the sawhorse as bullets whistled wildly through the mulberry grove. I knew something bad was wrong and I must have vaulted backward about ten feet. It also crossed my mind to dive behind the building.

Photo 3. Only once did the author see a weapon get away from Carbine Williams. This .30 caliber machine gun reared when initially fired. When it came down, it missed the saw horse and began to "dig a hole" in the ground. Fancy foot work and quick action brought the weapon under control.

Carbine held on firmly as the muzzle fell down between his feet and Ross', the bullets chopping up the ground and sending dirt showering fifteen feet into the air. Ross tried to jam the weapon by twisting the belt, but Carbine finally managed to get his finger off the trigger. What made it difficult was that it was a pistol grip trigger operated with one hand, and it would have been difficult to stop firing without risking dropping the gun completely, for the entire gun weight pulled against the trigger finger of the gunner.

I did manage to snap a picture just before the chopper stopped roaring, and while it was buried between their feet. (Photo 3) Initially, I didn't know whether or not I even had a photo. When Ross asked me about it, I said I thought I had taken one, but it could just as well have been a picture of the top of one of the mulberry trees.

There were no two ways about it — the experience shook Ross and left me petrified. Carbine? He was madder than hell, and wanted to clean out the mechanism and cut loose again. They did, but this time the gun was mounted on the tripod, at Ross' insistence.

By this time I was willing to call it quits, at least for this first session. I got to thinking that if a book were written on Carbine, it would be necessary for a good many of these little visits to take place. Was it worth it? After all, I had a wife and four children, all dependent on me to make at least some effort to live out my life expectancy.

Anyway, it was getting toward sundown and the temperature on this December 7 must have been below freezing. I mumbled something to Ross about heading home and he nodded. He asked Carbine if we could help put some of the prized weapons back into the smokehouse. Carbine, then seated on a trunk for the first time during the afternoon, said, "Yes, you can, Ross, but not him!"

"Him" meant me, and I stood around outside while Ross and Carbine transported the guns across the field. I didn't feel that it would be smart to remain alone in the shop while Carbine was gone, although that little pot-bellied stove felt like heaven. I stood outside, discreetly, freezing.

They remained in the smokehouse some twenty minutes, and when they returned Carbine invited me to leave the shop again because he wanted to talk to Ross about something privately. I went out and sat in the car for maybe forty more minutes, shivering as I watched doves sail into a corn field behind the mulberry grove. I thought about starting the car to let the heater run, but Ross had the keys in his pocket. It seemed the wiser course not to make an intrusion.

Finally, I saw the shades being drawn on all the windows. Carbine and Ross came out carrying two paper bags, which they put on the front seat, and a pair of Carbine's best rifles, which he had decided to take back to his home. After a double-check on the lock, they got into the car and we rode back to the cottage. My teeth chattered from both fright and cold.

Ross began taking in the guns while Carbine disappeared around the house for something. I loaded up all of our gear and Mrs. Williams gave me two large paper bags of pecans as gifts for our wives. I accepted them appreciatively, for I needed several pounds of pecans for my annual fruitcake-baking venture at Christmas. I soon regretted I had taken them, however.

Ross and I were at the gate, ready to make our departure, when Carbine returned. He was across the yard and it was dark, but he spied those two bags, one now in Ross' hands. It didn't take me long to realize the situation, and how it might look to Carbine. Those bags looked exactly like the ones we had brought back from his shop and which contained his fine pistols.

My heart sank as Carbine charged across the yard, swinging open his coat and exposing that holstered .45. He didn't say a word, although I was convinced he intended to see just what the hell was leaving in those bags. Ross and I piped up in unison, "Pecans! Pecans! Mrs. Williams gave us some pecans!" In unison we fished into the bags and produced a handful for all the world to see.

He still hadn't said a word, but he appeared satisfied. We climbed into the car, and slowly rolled out of the yard and onto highway 301. The inside of the car was a mess: tapes, parts of tape recorders all over the place; coats tangled; cameras, and parts, here and there. But that was the least of our worries; we were now on our way home, and I thought to myself that I would probably be willing to return once I recovered from the shock. At least I would spend another Christmas at home!

Ross and I spent the next three hours on the road, discussing the incredible happenings of that day. Ross is a pretty swift road-runner, and it is not uncommon that he makes his car passengers a little nervous. He doesn't particularly bother me, but on the way back he must have asked if his driving were worrying me.

"Ross," I said, "after what I've been through, if you missed that curve up ahead and ran straight through that cotton patch, I'd probably burst right out laughing because, truthfully, it would be the most relaxed moment I've spent today."

CHAPTER 3
The Early Years

The Williams Family

Over the years, every conceivable magazine and newspaper had published the same basic information about the legendary inventor, David Marshall "Carbine" Williams. That the true family background of this man had never been told came to light during an interview with Carbine's wife Maggie and one of his brothers, Shell. Contrary to the general assumption that the Williamses were "hillbillies," this large family, in reality, was fairly prosperous and well-educated. James Claud Williams, Carbine's father, was a prominent farmer, large landowner and civic leader in the Godwin area of Cumberland County (Photo 4).

The elder Williams had two families. By his first wife, nee Eula Lee Breece, there were four children: John, Mack, Will and Ruth. By the second Mrs. Williams, nee Laura Kornegay, there were seven children: Marshall (Carbine), Eula, Leon, Wesley, Sheldon "Shell", Eloise and Gordon. Most of this family is deceased now but the remaining members still carry the dignity and poise of proud and influential people in their county.

Among the prominent ancestors of Marshall Williams was William R. King, a great-great uncle who was a Vice-President of the United States (Photo 5).

The fifth generation of Williamses lives on the old farmplace. Grandpa was a large landowner, a very successful farmer. Even in the early days all of his children who desired to do so were sent to college. Most of them

Photo 4. Claud and Laura Williams, Carbine's parents, on their wedding day. This was Williams' second wife, nee Laura Kornegay, by which he had seven children. He had four children by an earlier marriage.

Photo 5. William Rufus King (1786-1853), Carbine's great-great uncle on his mother's side, was elected Vice President of the United States and would have served under President Franklin Pierce. However, he died of tuberculosis in Cuba before taking office.

Photo 6. At the age of 14, Williams entered a Cumberland County contest for producing the most corn per acre. He won a prize of a pocket knife for raising more than one hundred and ten bushels per acre.

went and all made good lives for themselves. As an example, son John (a bachelor until he was sixty-nine) became a very prominent businessman in Charlottesville, Virginia, and amassed a fortune during his lifetime. Maintaining a family interest, it was John who extended both personal and financial help to Marsh Williams and who initially helped him in getting the patent on his first .22 caliber machine gun after the inventor returned from prison and developed this weapon in a small shop on the old homeplace.

In talking with Miss Maggie, it quickly came to light that the Williamses were a very religious family. Early every morning at breakfast, there was a prayer and Bible reading. All of the family were required to be there and they had better have a good excuse if they were absent, for as Miss Maggie put it, "Grandpa would not hesitate to pull an ear." Miss Maggie added that she and Marsh continued the prayers and Bible readings in their own home.

James Claud Williams, Carbine's father, had specific duties for all of the boys, which primarily involved hard work on the farm. Most of the boys completed their work, but Marsh did not like farm work and avoided it whenever possible. He would slip away from the fields to the edge of the woods where he would sit and daydream about guns, for even in his early years this was his prime interest. His mother recalled that even as a child of three Marsh would carry a stick on his shoulder and march through the house saying, "Soldier, Mama, soldier." He was always interested in the military and military-related artifacts.

While Marshall Williams did not enjoy farm chores, he did like a challenge, any challenge. In the early 1900 s Cumberland County offered prizes to those who produced the most corn per acre. This appealed to Marsh Williams, about fourteen years old at the time, and he entered the contest (Photo 6). He won by raising more than one hundred and ten bushels per acre. Among his reasons for entering the contest was the prize of a fine pocket knife, for he often utilized a pocket knife to whittle out wooden

Photo 7. The rare times you saw the warmth of Williams' smile was when he was looking at his wife, "Maggie," his childhood sweetheart.

guns. He didn't have much use for one of the other prizes — a middle-buster plow.

Eight Grades

During my early interviews with Carbine Williams, I was quite uncertain as to what I should ask and what I would be better off leaving unquestioned. I could never anticipate his reaction to questions — especially personal ones. I did marvel at his technical knowledge and was often amazed at the extent and depth of his responses to questions. Finally, mustering up all my courage, being as tactful as possible and being sure that I was out of range of his arms and powerful fists, I asked him, "Be honest with me. What kind of education do you really have?" His eyes danced and a big smile flashed across his face as he replied: "Ross, I didn't go to but eight grades in school and, frankly, I got six of them because they wanted to get rid of me. I was no model student."

Carbine, however, was not lacking in intelligence. If he wanted to learn or do something, he unfailingly accomplished his aim. He liked to win. For example, when he was in the fifth grade, a prize was offered to the student who drew the best North Carolina flag. Marsh Williams won the contest and was awarded the prize he liked most — a shiny pocket knife.

Continuously restless, prowling the fields — disrupting school whenever possible, cutting school quite often — Marsh Williams became less and less interested in classroom education.

Young Maggie

Marsh did maintain one continuous interest in school — a classmate, Maggie, who was later to become his wife (Photo 7). He had two reasons for this interest. For one, he liked this pretty girl. A proud boy, he delighted in walking home with Miss Maggie. One time after holding her hand, he wrote her a note instructing, "Don't you dare tell I held your hand."

His second reason? He found it highly advantageous to sit behind Miss Maggie in school because she was a prize student. By peeking over her shoulder he could get answers to test questions for which he was not willing to study. Full of devilment, yes, but he always had an eye for beauty, and his definition of beauty, even at that early age, included the specification that his girl must not only be pretty to look at but must have a sense of humor and an understanding of a boy's way of thinking. And she definitely could not be a tattletale type. These characteristics he found in his Maggie.

Marsh left little doubt in anyone's mind that Maggie was his girl. To insure his position in the eyes of this young lady, he made sure, whenever he did decide to go to school, that he carried Maggie's books. A great deal of Marsh's energies and attentions were diverted to Maggie, and more and more time was spent in her company — calling at the house, walking with her, sitting and talking about the dreams they both had for the future and becoming more and more fond of one another.

Marsh's courting days provided a period of relaxation and peace of mind for the folks in and around Godwin, for which all were appreciative.

Wooden Guns

Although he courted heavily, Marsh Williams never failed to find time for his friends — one in particular, a young man by the name of Roy McLamore. From all indications, Roy was " all boy" and Marsh, and the two were normally side by side when anything exciting was underway locally.

"I got Roy into the wooden gun making business," Carbine recalled. "I remember a good joke I played on Roy.

"It was a hot summer's day," he continued, "and Roy's dad had come in from work and was taking a nap before dinner. Roy wanted to convince his dad that this was a pretty good gun. It was one of our 'shotguns.' We put up a target, loaded the gun and called Roy's dad. His father was slow about getting up, and Roy didn't believe that he was coming, so we decided to go ahead and shoot anyway. We did, but I had overloaded the gun with powder and it blew back in Roy's face. Man! He looked like he had been sprinkled with black pepper.

"We both both took off running for the woods, and it was at that same moment that Roy's dad came out of the door and yelled for Roy to come back. Roy stopped, but I was already in the woods and I kept running. Roy headed back for the house and I don't know what happened to him; but I can well imagine!"

Setting the Woods on Fire

There was dense forest around the Williams' house and the children spent much of their time running through the woods shooting homemade guns.

"One time at recess at school when the woods were very, very dry," Carbine recalled, "we shot and the explosion from our guns set the woods on fire. We darned near burned the whole place down, and you should have seen folks from all around turning out to fight the fire. They got things under control after awhile, but they never found out that it was our shooting that caused all of the trouble. It would have been too bad if Dad had found out that I had any part of this."

First Store-Bought Weapon

The wooden guns' not being as dependable and accurate as he desired, Marsh Williams soon saved the money necessary to order his first store-bought pistol.

"I remember when I was just fourteen years old I decided that I wanted a real pistol," he reminisced. "So I got up $16.75, somehow, and ordered a .45 caliber double-action Colt revolver. It had a seven and a half inch barrel. I ordered if from Colt's factory of Hartford, Connecticut, and I went down and picked it up from the post office. I carried that big old pistol to school with me," he continued in confidential tone. "I can remember sitting up there with that big pistol on my side in the schoolroom right beside Maggie. At recess we would run out to the woods and shoot my pistol.

"I didn't go to school too much," he continued, "but when I went I had a good time. I finally finished the eighth grade and decided that I just had enough of school."

Episode at Ezell's Blacksmith Shop

After Carbine left school, he worked for awhile at Ezell's Blacksmith Shop. "One day a fellow brought in his T-Model Ford, and I was told to make some adjustments under the car," Carbine reminisced. " I was still carrying my Colt double-action .45 with the seven and a half inch barrel, and to keep dirt from getting into my pistol I took it out of my back pocket and stuck the barrel up into the frame of the T-Model until I had finished my work.

"The front sight was a big one so that it easily held the heavy pistol in place," he continued. "Being a habitual 'gun toter' you forget whether you have your weapon in your pocket or not. When I finished my work, I crawled out from under the car and left my pistol. The owner drove off in his T-Model with my .45 still stuck up in the frame before I remembered that it was under there.

"I figured that he might have stopped at Mr. C.W. Spell's general store, so I took off running to get down there in case he stopped. He had stopped his car in front of the store, and there were a bunch of folks standing around in front of the store when I arrived. I didn't say anything. I just rolled under that car and there she was, still stuck up in the frame. I got my pistol, crawled out from under the man's car, put the pistol in my pocket and walked away.

"Folks around that store were sure curious as to why in the world I had run that far just to roll up under that car that way," he smiled.

Interest in Gun Making

While going through a number of photographs with Carbine one morning, we came across his baby picture. I kidded him, noting that from the little bulge under his baby gown, it appeared that he had a pistol hidden there. He laughed heartily. Following this up I asked, "Actually Carbine, about how old were you when you began to realize that you had a serious interest in firearms?"

"Being raised on a farm I naturally thought about guns all the time," he replied. "As a boy I shot rabbits and romped in the fields of my dad's plantation, and often saw the grown folks hunting up in the fields. As a young man I always sported pistols. Everyone knew that, too," he said with a smile. "Weren't nothing new about this at all. I was always fascinated with the insides of things, especially guns. I used to take my guns apart and put them together many times and was always fascinated by the inner workings.

"Folks [when writing about me later] would tell about my first thinking about inventing or making guns while I was in prison. That just isn't true. I thought about them plenty down on that farm, that's for sure. But while in the dark hole [solitary confinement at Caledonia Prison, located near Halifax, North Carolina, very close to the Virginia-North Carolina state line], I was thinking about them to get my mind off the pain and discomfort of that box I was chained inside of. I'll tell you plenty about that later," he promised.

"To tell you something about my inventing, I must tell you something about my family." Coughing amid a cloud of cigarette smoke, he continued, "You see, there have been inventors in our family before. One, Jule King, used to come right here to Godwin when I was a boy and work on his inventions. He invented different kinds of farm machinery and built them right here in the blacksmith shop. I used to be fascinated how he could draw a wheel or a gear and make it stand out on a piece of paper. Everything I drew just appeared to be awfully flat. I guess that some of my inventive ability may have come from ol' Jule King, an uncle of my mother."

Photo 8. Williams, along with two friends, joined the Navy as teen-agers. "I just, frankly, didn't 'gee-haw' with the Navy," he admitted.

Photo 9. After his return home from the Navy, Williams was enrolled for a short period at Blackstone Military Academy in Virginia.

A Stint in the Navy

Carbine's working for Ezell's Blacksmith shop and tinkering around with guns was not Claud Williams' idea of what a young man should be doing. Understanding the need for an education for his son and recognizing that Marsh was militarily inclined, he finally agreed to allow Marsh to lie about his age and join the United States Navy. Marsh Williams thought this would be the answer to all his needs and all his dreams. He was so exuberant about this opportunity that he discussed it at length with his friends and, as so often happens among close boyhood friends, several of the boys joined the Navy with him (Photo 8).

"Ross, I entered the Navy when I was about sixteen," Carbine related. "No reason in the world why I decided to be in the Navy. It just seemed to happen. Two friends were there too. They went with me — Roy McLamore, of course, my old friend, and Ernest Ennis, both from around Godwin.

"The family didn't think much about the idea of us going and they liked even less the fact we fibbed about our ages a little. It wasn't like my son David, who served on the *Canberra*, a Navy showpiece, an elite ship, one of the missile carriers. All I remember was that I was assigned to a Company Y; and this was a pretty rough company, I'm telling you. I don't know where these men and boys came from. Our commanding officer said that we were a disgrace to the United States Navy. That's exactly what he said, Ross. The ones of us that weren't in the brig were AWOL. There weren't hardly enough of us left to hold guard duty. At one time I had to pull guard duty two times in one night. I was thoroughly disgusted. It was just a damn mess for a young boy.

"But even under these conditions we managed to have some fun," he continued. "At one time I wanted to go into Berkeley, and everyone else on the ship had a pass but me. I'd be almost to the guard and I would run past him. I'd wait until about fifty sailors were milling around and then

I'd run into them and hide so that they couldn't recognize me. Then, when I had to come back in, there was a great fence which you couldn't climb. The boys would get together and help me over it and I would outrun the guards and hit the hammocks. Ross, they *knowed* I was there. I wasn't any specialty, but they *knowed* I was there.

"I remember one time on the rifle range we were supposed to be learning how to shoot and I outshot everybody," Marsh boasted. "The officers assumed that I must be from the Blue Ridge Mountains. I figured that there was a good angle to this so, when asked, I immediately lied and said, 'Yes sir.' First thing I had to do was to figure out what county I should say I was from. So I selected Graham County. I told them I was from there and not Cumberland. I had to become a 'squirrel shooter' in their eyes right away, because that's what the man said and it seemed that's what he wanted.

"I just, frankly, didn't 'gee-haw' with the Navy," he concluded. "I contacted the family and my father had contact with Congressmen in the area, and because I was underage they managed to work it out that I could get out of the Navy honorably. About all I remember today about the Navy, Ross, or any association that I had with it, is the fact that each time I bless our meal I do say, 'God bless all the ships at sea.'"

From Military School to Marriage

On Marsh's return to Godwin, where he was still restless and causing havoc in the community, it was Claud Williams' idea that possibly a military school would answer the needs and fulfill the desires of his son. So enrollment was arranged for him in 1917 at Blackstone Military Academy in Virginia. Amazingly enough, at first, Marshall Williams flourished there. He liked his uniform and he took a great interest in his classes and in the daily military routine (Photo 9). His commanding officers predicted that he would make a fine officer in the military. But the lad's interest waned.

"Ross, I don't know what happened to Marsh. He seemed to get homesick," Maggie explained when asked about Carbine's stay at the military school. "He did something up there that he never would tell us about, and they sent him home. He was expelled."

"Miss Maggie," I asked, "was there any possibility that Marsh was in love with you, and that he did something intentionally so that he could come home and be with his loved one?"

"Ross," she said, laughing, "people have said this and Marsh has said this but I just don't know."

My research uncovered only one letter written by Marsh while at Blackstone Military Academy. In this letter to his beloved mother Marsh confided, "I am becoming a man now and I hope that someday I can get a little house and make a good home for tiny Miss Maggie. I hope that I can soon marry her if she will have me. I may not succeed but as long as I live nobody else will have her."

Obviously it was his love for Miss Maggie that drove Marsh to leave the military school and come home to the one he loved. After attending only one semester, on August 11, 1918, on a Sunday morning, David Marshall Williams married Margaret Isobel Cook at her home. His sister Eula played, "I Love You Truly" and "To a Wild Rose" on an old-fashioned pump organ. The Reverend A.R. McQueen performed the ceremony. The bride and groom left immediately from the wedding ceremony for the regular morning service at Godwin Presbyterian Church, riding in style as newlyweds in a Model-T Ford. There was no honeymoon. A home was furnished and awaited occupancy by the couple at Godwin.

"Grandpa had lots of small lots and homes in the area and provided one of these for our first home," Carbine explained.

CHAPTER 4
Whiskey Days

Working on the ACL

Following his marriage, Carbine Williams took a job with the Atlantic Coast Line Railroad.

"Ross, the work was hard and the hours were long," Carbine sighed, recalling the laborious days. "Needless to say, it was most disillusioning to a young man. I was making fourteen cents an hour to start with. This was a ten-hour day. I was sick of the poor pay so I looked for something else to do.

"A man working on the railroad put me in touch with another man in Fayetteville whose job was making liquor stills," he continued. "He ran a tin shop right off of the main street in Fayetteville. He made good stills, too. First, I talked to him about getting a job building stills. And then I started questioning him about how much money I could make producing whiskey as compared to how much he could pay me to make stills. Fort Bragg being in the vicinity [it] offered a ready market for good whiskey."

Decision to Make Whiskey

"In a short time I decided that my field would be whiskey making," Carbine continued. "One of my colored men and I went to Fayetteville at night and picked up the still. We covered it with a tarpaulin in the back of a wagon and started back. Now, Ross, our wagon had a warped wheel and it squeaked. God almighty it squeaked! This caused the still to vibrate. A sort of continuous roaring came about as we rolled on out of town. Nobody paid any attention — those were the good ole days, Ross, people paid attention to their own business.

"I operated this still a long, long time and Miss Maggie never found out, not until I was burned," Williams recalled, his blue eyes dancing. "While I was running the still somebody told me to put dried apples in the Dublin keg to make the whiskey taste better, and so I did. I was always one to experiment. The steam couldn't go through because the apples swelled up and the still wouldn't run. I knew the whiskey should be coming out of the worm but it just wasn't. So I pulled the fire out from under that kettle and gave it time to cool down enough to pull the cap off the still. (It was still under pressure because the steam couldn't go through the apples in the Dublin keg.) When I pulled the cap off, the boiling beer come rolling out right on the top of the collar of the still and burned half of my face and cooked my left arm.

"I had a kinda big Indian working for me and he was trying to get my clothes off," he continued. "He was a strong man and I had on strong clothes, and he would grunt. I could hear him. I was burned sho' enough. I went to his daddy's house, which was not so far, and the old man was telling me that he had a remedy for my burns. He sent his boy back down to the still and brought a gallon of that strong whiskey back to the house. And I went into the parlor and stayed there half a day.

"He had me to wash my face in that whiskey. I could feel the left side of my face drawing," Carbine said with a grimmace. "I'd take a pocket knife and scrape it, and wash it, and scrape it again. I wondered how in the world I would look with my face all drawed up. It didn't, but for years there were big scars on my arm. I wouldn't go to the doctor and Maggie helped me dress my burned arm. I didn't want her to know too much about that. I didn't want to go to the doctor either because he knew Pa. I would have blisters come on my arm about like a partridge egg. I would take my knife and cut them. It was a mess but I got well. It was

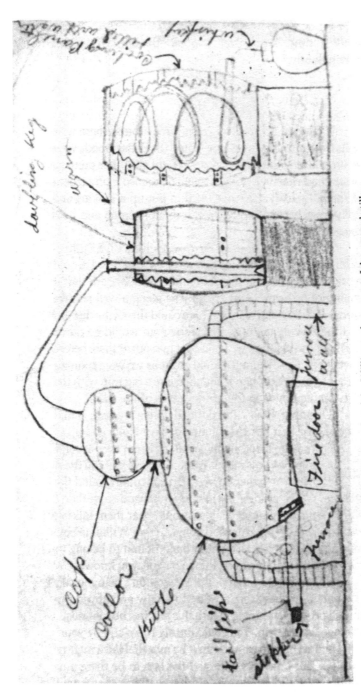

Photo 10. This sketch by Williams shows one of the several stills he operated in the vicinity of Godwin, N.C. His dealing in moonshine whiskey eventually led to his indictment for murder when a deputy sheriff was slain while raiding his still.

quite a time. I got over it good, though," he added nonchalantly.

Five Holly

"I covered about three miles' area around there with stills from my home location (Photo 10). Dense woods were all around here then. We had about eight sites. The prettiest place I had was Five Holly. Somebody named it on account of the holly trees. I always liked to put up a still around holly trees because holly trees seemed to catch and hold the smoke.

"I remember putting down a well at Five Holly," Williams continued. "Usually we used a pump. I would work on the pump so that it would run so smooth that it could not be heard. This time I was using a well six feet across. We dug down as far as we could throw the dirt out and then we dynamited. Ross, one man would go down and light the fuse and we would get him out of there before it went off. The dynamite would go off as we were running through the woods, and it sounded like a big rain with the dirt coming down on top of the leaves of the trees.

"One time, Ross," he confided with a sly grin, "I had a lot of beer that needed running at Five Holly and all of the fellows were standing by to run it. From over around Falcon some Holiness people came. I believe you call them 'Holy Rollers.' Yes, they came and accidentally found the still site. We were hiding out in the woods because we didn't want to hurt no church people. I could hear them talking and one said, 'Yes, I know it belongs to that Williams boy, for them barrels are all right in line.' Bound to belong to me 'cause I had done everything so neat, you know.

"My men got scared and they wouldn't help me run this batch for they were afraid of the law and afraid the church people were going to turn this still in," he continued. "No one would help. You could hardly run a still by yourself. But I went in there and run it by myself. Had a mighty hard job but I did it. I expected the law to be there any minute. My still being marked by neatness they knew whose it was. Everything was as nice, as clean, as a woman cooking in her kitchen," he said with pride.

"Ross, moonshining in those days was not like a lot of people would think. We weren't desperadoes. We boys would run over to Five Holly and we'd get us a fire going and we'd cook out and eat and some of the boys would be picking a banjo. As you know, I play a fiddle a little and I enjoyed this. And if we suddenly decided to let out a whoop and holler we would. Those were the good times," Marsh reminisced.

"Frankly, though, I had so much whiskey over there — you would have to sample it — I just got so sick of tasting whiskey that once when I started to Godwin one night, I had a pint bottle in my pocket, and being so disgusted with it, I pulled the bottle out of my pocket and put it beside the road. I couldn't even bear the thought of toting whiskey. I was just sick of it," he said, shaking his head in disgust.

The Feds Come

"The local police were all right, but the federal boys were a different story," Carbine revealed. "They got after me one time. We almost had a small war near Godwin that time. There was plenty of hard talk going on there, Ross. It almost came to gun fire. They came there to search my house and I didn't have no whiskey there. It was all in the woods close by. I did have the cap of a whiskey still in there though, in the back room. They wanted to look around, and I said go ahead and look. One of the federal men looked in there and saw the cap and he got plumb hot under the collar but he had sense enough not to say too much. Yeah, it was hot because both of us was geared for a fight.

"As a matter of fact," Carbine continued, as though it were yesterday, "there was a little outbuilding there and my Maggie got so disgusted with these carryings-on that she decided to go there to get out of the storm. One of the federal men decided that he would be a smart aleck and follow her and see where she was going and what she was going out there for. Ross, I cussed him good. I don't know what I told him, but it was plenty. I said, 'You go another God damned step further, mister, and I'll kill you!' He turned around and I would have shot him just as sure as hell. That's one God damned time that I would have shot him deader than hell. I drawed the line and he took it. It just ended there and he went on. I'm glad of that."

The visit by federal agents confirmed to Miss Maggie beyond the shadow of a doubt that Marshall was, indeed, making moonshine whiskey. Young, in love and a strong woman, she was determined to put an end to this. Maggie sent for Marsh's brother Leon. Together they stood on the railroad tracks in the heart of Godwin and from there watched the smoke rising from Marsh's still in the nearby woods. Together they decided that they would dynamite the still.

"That same day in the afternoon I went to the still," Leon recalled. "It was the first time that I ever visited any of Marsh's stills. I was actually 'casing' the still for the purpose of blowing it up. When I got near the still I hailed Marsh. Marsh answered. I said, 'This is Leon.' Marsh said, 'Come on in.'

"I noticed as I entered the area that everyone had Krag rifles. They were all alike. Almost instantly he handed me a gun. 'We may have visitors today,' he warned. Knowing that the local officers were quite friendly I asked, 'Do you mean the law?' 'Yes,' he replied.

"Ross, what I am going to tell you now is true," Leon continued. "Marsh commented during my visit to the still that Al Pate [the deputy sheriff Williams was later convicted of slaying] owed him $75 for whiskey. Now I don't know if this was true or if Al Pate had bought whiskey for himself or for others or as evidence, but Marsh did make this statement to me."

Local Authorities Whistle

"The local authorities weren't as anxious to bother us [as the federals]," Carbine explained. "Somebody would report a still in operation and they'd be obliged to come out. We had a pretty good system going, however. Someone in the local sheriff's office would call a certain store in Godwin and let 'em know that they were coming. When they did, they would ring an old farm bell and this was a signal for us to get out of there.

"I had some good and faithful men working for me and one of them, Charlie Smith, used to help me make 'recipes.' He was a black man. He is still living and is about ninety years old now. There's another fellow named Ham Dawson who was one of the crew.

"Getting back to the local officials," he continued, "they not only didn't bother us too often, but they seemed to like to come down to the still. Now we were all armed at that time and one time I was carrying a Newton rifle. Now this is one of the longest-range rifles in the world. It was very nearly double the striking power and energy at fifteen hundred yards as the .30-'06 Army rifle.

"Anyhow, I was running one of the stills over yonder. We'll call it Mack Riles' place, on a branch. It was a pretty good place. I was at the still and all of a sudden one of the sheriffs that knew me, a friend of mine, came running in toward the still. He didn't give the usual signal, a whistle we knew. All I seen was him coming running and the Newton was standing beside the great black gum tree. So I just reached for it and *then* he begun whistling. He whistled *loud*. He sure did like to come around there when we were making liquor. I won't call his name. He was a good sheriff though, a deputy sheriff. He didn't think nothing about our making liquor 'cause we were good friends. We hung around and had a pretty good time together.

"When I'd go to the still at Five Holly, and I had a big one there," Carbine revealed, "on the way over I used to like to stop by ah old colored man's home, called Uncle Joe Williams. I'd sit around that old log house, warm up, and just stay there awhile and then go on. He liked my Newton rifle. I had a lot of fun with that rifle. I could do a lot of mighty powerful fine shooting with it, as you know. I was especially good in them days," he declared with warranted pride.

Wood Pays Good but Liquor Is Quicker

"One thing that always amused me, Ross," Carbine grinned, "there was some fellows that used to cut wood and load supplies on the train at Godwin. Now they'd work all week and bring all those logs down to the train. While they were working on loading that train on one end, I'd have one of my boys putting a croaker sack full of moonshine whiskey on the back. They'd put it back there in the caboose for the railroad officials. I made good whiskey, and I also made as much money with that croaker sack as those fellows did working all day long loading wood on that train. I also delivered a powerful bunch of whiskey to the sheriff's office in Fayetteville during them days, too, to certain fellows."

Carbine's brother Shell confirmed that Marsh was always able to procure the necessary copper and coils for his stills through a connection in the sheriff's office. Obviously, this material came from other whiskey stills destroyed in and around Cumberland County.

The Spirit Meter

"Ross, what we're looking at here is the case for what we call the spirit meter (Photo 11). It is a gauge that you used to tell what proof your whiskey was. When whiskey comes out of a whiskey still, at first it comes out around one hundred and forty proof. The more you ran it, each time it got weaker and weaker and it'd run down, and then it got below a hundred. Then it'd get about ninety and it'd turn into what we called 'low wines.' That's what the old-timers said, low wines. You was supposed to quit then, because until it got to the low wines it would be nice and clear like distilled water. Once it turned into low wine and got so low in proof, it looked cloudy, kinda milky-like. Well then you'd quit, you know. I never did run any low wine at all," he said with satisfaction.

"The spirit meter that went in this case here was my gauge to measure the proof of my whiskey, and when I'd

Photo 11. "This is the case for my spirit gauge. Using this gauge, I tested the proof of my whiskey. They say I made the best in the country. It was never sold if it was under 103 proof."

go to sell it, it'd be certain to be at least one hundred and three proof. You knew what you were getting."

I encouraged Carbine to describe the gauge: "You were telling me that it started with a small glass cylinder and then increased in size to a round bulb at the bottom, very much like a thermometer," I reminded him.

"Yes," he continued, "the bottom of it enlarged to give it buoyancy in the liquor, and in the stem was a piece of paper with proof calibrations. Some fine shot in the little ball section at the bottom — held in place by a little piece of cotton stuffed on top of the shot — weighted it at the bottom so it would float upright. With this gauge you knew what you were getting. Of course, an experienced man could tell a lot about proof from tasting."

The Miller Loved Liquor

"Talking about making good whiskey, you got to have something good to make it out of, including a good still," Carbine impressed upon me, "and know how to do it, and be willing to do it. You can't be in a hurry, scared somebody's gonna come in, and run it too fast. Do it right! In making good whiskey, you had to make good beer, and to make good beer you had to have good old-fashioned corn malt. You'd get your corn, good corn, ripe corn in the grain, you know, like you're gonna take it to a mill to make meal, and then you'd sprout it. You'd sprout it until it'd be about a half inch long, and you'd dry the corn, sprout and all. Then you'd take it to a mill and grind it, like you would corn meal.

"I remember one time I said to my men, 'Boys, our beer is ready for the malt now and the miller is scared to grind it. It's getting tight around here now.' And they said, 'Yes, we know that,' or something like that."

"Wasn't the miller near Dunn, North Carolina?" I asked.

"Yes, he was about four miles north of here, this side of Dunn, at what they call Rhodes Mill," he confirmed. "It's still marked Rhodes Pond but we call it Rhodes Mill.

They had an old-fashioned water mill there with the old-fashioned rocks.

"While we're talking about it, I used to help sharpen them rocks—me and the fellow who ran the blacksmith shop. We tempered the chisels and we sharpened them rocks.

"Anyway, getting back to the malt, we had to grind it and we had a few bushels there that we just had to have, that's all. It was time for it. We went there and the miller was afraid to grind it. So we went there one night, raised a window, went in, used lanterns and flashlights, and ground our own malt. And in that old mill you could have heard it a mile, I reckon," he said with a chuckle. "It was a still summer night and them old wooden gears would say, *Wong! Wong! Wong! Wong!* The people would be going by the road about twenty steps from there and they wouldn't even stop. We'd be having us a good time drinking, you know. Once in a while we'd shoot a time or two and holler good and loud; everybody would be having a good time, a real good time. Well, we ground it and shut it down and went on about our business," Carbine said without a trace of guilt.

"We left some good liquor in there. We knew the miller loved liquor. Well who don't like good liquor? Especially the kind I made—very good. But that particular liquor we had at that time was especially good, better than at other times. It seemed like at some times it tasted a little bit better. I forget how much we left, about a half gallon," Marsh estimated.

"Did the miller know you were in there?" I asked.

"Oh yes. I told him that we were going ahead and grind our own malt. I also suggested that he would be wise to go on to sleep."

Fun Ends, Trouble Begins

Life was not to remain tranquil, and Carbine was not to continue to enjoy the days of whiskey making—the hollering, the singing and the cooking out, as he described it. He was in violation of the law. On July 21, 1921, a raid on his still took place and his whiskey-making days ended in tragedy.

"Ross, it all happened like a clap of thunder," Carbine recalled. "It was fast moving. Six of my men and I were at the still when the deputies came in shooting—and they came in fast. It was every man for himself. Bullets were flying. We all ran and hid in the woods. I stayed in the woods a number of places that evening and night.

"I remembered there was a log cabin way back over in the woods when I left the raid," he continued. "I sneaked up to that cabin and I heard some people talking inside. Now, Ross, this was a friendly cabin. They were my friends. I wasn't going in, however, because I didn't know who was in there. I listened, and I knew voices. I just listened. I knew their names and I knew that they would protect me, but I would not go in and involve them.

"Ross, you will never know the feeling or the thoughts that run through a man's mind when he's hunted. It's an exultant feeling in a way. You've made up your mind that you are a desperado, that you're gonna shoot it out if they come after you. You make arrangements for turpentine to put on your feet 'cause you know this will throw the scent off if the bloodhounds come after you. You trust no one. As an example, it happened that during the night one of the family, Leon, came through the woods to see me. I was still trusting no one. Frankly, I was somewhat scared," Carbine admitted. "Ross, you don't think about yesterday and you don't think about tomorrow when you're in a situation like this.

"As I saw Leon approaching, I had in my hands a very high-powered rifle. I very calmly cocked this rifle and let him walk right into the muzzle of it and actually bump it. He was a strong man. He spoke first and I didn't speak. He brought me a message from Mother telling me that she thought I should surrender and not run. Having received this word, I made up my mind then that I would surrender, and I sent word back by Leon to make the necessary arrangements. Also, late in the night I sneaked through the

67

Photo 12. When Williams was taken into custody following the slaying of Deputy Sheriff Al J. Pate, he was held at this jail in Raeford, N.C., "because Fayetteville had such an old jail."

Photo 13. The headline of the July 23, 1921, *Fayetteville Observer* focused on the arrest of Williams. He turned himself in to Sheriff N.H. McGeachy.

woods and went back to Father's home and saw Ma and Pa. I talked to them and then I went to see my Maggie at her parents' house."

Carbine continued his revelation of events of the night preceding his arrest: "Word was sent to the sheriff that they could meet me in Godwin that morning. And so it was arranged. Father and his lawyer, Nat Townsend, went there with me. He had come down from Dunn. He sensed that I had not fully made up my mind as to whether I should surrender or not, and he looked at me quite sternly and I will never forget his words: 'He who tarries is lost.'

"The lawyer knew time was running out because there were people on the way then, the sheriff and his deputies. So I agreed that I would surrender, and I did. The sheriff and his men arrived. They took me into custody, and because Fayetteville had such an old jail, they decided to take me to Raeford, North Carolina, to a new jail (Photo 12). When we got there, Sheriff McGeachy, who knew me to be a man of my word, looked at me and very casual-like said, 'Marsh, do you have a gun on you?' And I said, 'No, Sheriff,' and that was all there was. I was not searched."

On July 23, 1921, banner headlines in the *Fayetteville Observer* screamed: MARSHALL WILLIAMS ARRESTED FOR KILLING DEPUTY AL J. PATE" (Photo 13). This was the first of numerous headlines in the coming days as a consequence of the raid on Carbine Williams' still.

Fayetteville Observer
Fayetteville, North Carolina   July 23, 1921
MARSHALL WILLIAMS ARRESTED FOR KILLING
DEPUTY AL J. PATE

Father of young man and brother-in-law turned him over to Sheriff McGeachy. Raiding party of county officers had torn up still of notorious man and were coming out of woods when they were fired upon. Pate is the fourth deputy killed in last year.

Marshall Williams, son of J. Claud Williams of near Godwin, was arrested by N. H. McGeachy about noon for the murder of Deputy Sheriff Al Pate which occurred last night in raiding Williams's still at Godwin. In answer to a telegram, the Sheriff carried Deputy Patrick and special officers Benton and Benderman to Godwin, and just as their car turned the corner of Charles Spell's home the Sheriff ordered it to stop. He got out and walked around toward the store and in just a few minutes came back announcing that it was all right. Marshall was being brought to him. Soon a car drove up containing J. Claud Williams, father of the young man, Columbus McClellan, brother-in-law of the young man, and Marshall himself. The Sheriff placed the young man under arrest and carried him to some unknown jail [Raeford Jail] for safekeeping. It is presumed they carried him to the State Prison at Raleigh. Deputy Patrick and the other officer returned to the city this afternoon.

Al J. Pate, for twenty years or more a deputy sheriff of Cumberland County, one of the bravest officers ever connected with the sheriff's office here, was shot to death last night by a moonshiner, believed to be Marshall Williams, the son of J. Claud Williams, of near Godwin. After the still had been raided, an outfit including a big still, thirty gallons of liquor, and much beer had been captured. Mr. Pate was about sixty years of age and leaves a widow and four children. He was a member of the raiding party, consisting of Sheriff N. H. McGeachy, Deputy Bill West, Deputy Driver, himself, and George West, the latter driving the car.

They left this city in the neighborhood of 6 o'clock and drove to Godwin, a distance of twelve miles. They found the still within a very short distance of the little village of Godwin. Smoke from the still could be seen from the railroad station. The officers drove to the place, which was on the Godwin-Falcon Road, not a far distance from Dunn Road. Leaving the car in the road in charge of George West, they made their way to the still through the dense bushes. As they got within seeing distance, three men were plainly seen at the place. Suddenly a voice was heard, 'Halt! Who is that?' But the officers were too close on them to stop. Sheriff McGeachy said that it was a case of stopping and being all killed or making a dash on the operators. So they sprang up through the bushes within a few yards of the still and the three men fled. Two big army rifles were left behind as they departed. The officers then proceeded to tear up the outfit. A call was sent to George West to bring the car as near as he could to load the loot in it, which he did. As soon as the car was loaded, Deputy Pate stepped up on the running board and sat down on the still, which was laying against the back seat, leaving the door open, and the car started back toward the road. Sheriff McGeachy and Deputies West and Driver were walking ahead of the automobile when suddenly shots began to ring out. One bullet grazed almost the tip of the Sheriff's nose and the second came so close to Deputy West's face that it burned him. They dropped to the ground, both for protection and to make the assassins think that they had been shot. The third bullet struck Deputy Pate at the right side just above the waistline and passing clear through his body coming out near the heart on the left side. The bullet severed the main artery on his left side. The fourth bullet fired went through Mr. Pate's hat and it toppled off. These two bullets also struck the steering wheel and how West escaped still remains a mystery. The fifth bullet went into the car.

In a few minutes Sheriff McGeachy came around the car where Deputy Pate had been hurt. He took hold of Mr. Pate's arm, shook him, and calling him at the same time, but no answer came back. Then he called to the driver to get out as rapidly as possible and get the wounded man to a doctor. They rushed to Dr. J. W. McLean's house and he told the Sheriff that Pate was instantly killed.

Sheriff McGeachy then went to Marshall Williams's house, carrying the guns he found at the still, and showed them to Mrs. Williams, asking her if she could say whether they belonged to her husband, but she declined to say. He then told her to tell Marshall the best thing to do was to come up and surrender. The Sheriff then went after Columbus McClellan, son of Chris McClellan, near Rhodes Mill, a brother-in-law of Williams, and a man named Ezell who operates a blacksmith shop with Williams. They were charged with spiriting Williams away and were brought back to the city and questioned closely.

The dead officer was brought to Rogers & Breece Undertakers to be prepared for burial. About ten o'clock this morning, the Sheriff received a telegram to come back to Godwin and in company with Deputy Patrick, Special Officers Benderman and Benton, returned to the scene of the shooting in the hope of finding Williams. According to reports, Marshall Williams had been for years almost a desperado and for some time citizens have lived in fear of their lives at his hands. He has sold liquor openly and defied the good citizens there to open their mouths about it. A church there has been his center of activity.

Deputy Pate made the fifth officer under Sheriff McGeachy to be shot down during the past twelve months and the fourth to surrender his life in the performance of his duty, Deputy Patrick being the one to survive. He had always been known as a fearless officer, one who knew nothing but duty and feared absolutely nothing. He always got his man when sent after a prisoner. Once he landed his man he was good to him. He had a heart as big as he was himself and loved to be of service to his fellow man. He was devoted to Sheriff McGeachy and was always ready at all times to face death with his chief. He bore on his face scars, placed there by the knives of men who sought to kill him. His body carried bullet wounds sent by would-be assassins. In self-defense he shot two men down, but with it all, Al Pate was as tender as a child.

The death of Deputy Sheriff Al Pate removes one of the most characteristic men who has ever held office at this court house. He regarded every man as his friend and there is much indignation of the shooting down of this fine officer. His body will be removed to his home during the day and the funeral will be held tomorrow afternoon at five o'clock. The burial will be in Gee Burial Ground in the back of the Widow's Home. One of the saddest features of his death is the fact that his daughter, who was married a week ago, is off on her honeymoon. She was married to Sergeant Stephens of Camp Bragg.

The *Fayetteville Observer* about this time initiated a campaign against crime and violence in Cumberland County and, as a part of it, again and again carried headlines and detailed accounts of Williams' arrest, relating the tragic effects on the Pate family and providing the gory details of the shooting. In so doing it stressed the general lawlessness and violence prevalent in the county and, willingly or not, became a factor in prejudicing the community against Williams as preparations for a trial began.

Fayetteville Observer
Fayetteville, North Carolina   July 23, 1921
Editorial: David B. Lindsey, Publisher
BRING THE MURDERER TO JUSTICE

The slaying of Deputy A. J. Pate Friday night by a supposed blockade distiller has caused sorrow and indignation throughout the community and county. An officer of the law with a record of twenty years faithful service is shot from ambush while in the discharge of his duty. A household is made desolate. The law is set at defiance and murder is added to violation of the prohibition law. It matters not whether one be in favor of or opposed to prohibition. The fact that blood had been shed by law violators is the supreme issue now. And it is the duty of every citizen of the country to uphold by voice and deed the Sheriff in the discharge of duty and in his efforts to bring the murderer or murderers to justice. Four deputy sheriffs killed and another desperately wounded within four months is a record which equals the worst section of the greatest cities. The courts and the people should see that a stop is put to such an alarming condition of affairs. How will they do it? The courts and jury should see that the guilty are punished and the people should set their faces as a flint against law violations.

On July 22, 1921, the day before Marshall Williams gave himself up, the headlines in the *Fayetteville Observer* gave firm evidence as to the strong anti-crime sentiment that was building in Cumberland County. The public was well aware of, and very concerned about, the daily crimes committed in their county.

The following three news stories and editorials of the time leave little doubt that violation of the law was daily routine, and from these accounts it is evident that the public had decided that it would no longer tolerate lawlessness.

Fayetteville Observer
Fayetteville, North Carolina   July 22, 1921
CRIME IN CUMBERLAND DEMANDS MOST DRASTIC PUNISHMENT LAW GIVES
by Fred W. Vaughan

Cumberland County has not been slighted by the crime wave which seems to be enveloping the entire country. The gunmen of the county are to be credited with another notch 'upon their stick' already full of indications which speak volumes for lawlessness and disregard of human life. The latest victim of the assassin's bullet was an efficient and trustworthy officer of the law, who when shot down was engaged in the discharge of his duty. It begins to look as though the policy of an eye for an eye and a tooth for a tooth must be invoked if the lawlessness in Cumberland County is to be abated. Human life is held too cheaply in Cumberland County.

Fayetteville Observer
Fayetteville, North Carolina   July 25, 1921
LOCAL PASTOR FLAYS LAWLESSNESS HERE AND PLEAS FOR RIGHT LIVING

Tributes paid to Deputy Pate by enormous crowd. Funeral of slain Deputy Sheriff attended by one of the largest crowds this city has ever seen here. Bold address by Reverend J.S. Snyder. Floral tributes beautiful.

One of the largest crowds that ever attended a funeral in Fayetteville paid its tributes Sunday afternoon to the memory of Al J. Pate, the deputy who went to his death at the hands of an assassin while in the performance of his duty in enforcing the law of this great nation. Every walk in life was represented at this service to great crowds standing in the large front yard with bared heads, while the Reverend Joel S. Snyder, pastor of the First Baptist Church, conducted the service.

Not only was the outpouring a tribute to the faithful officer of the law who had been slain, but it was a demonstration of the disapproval of the reign of lawlessness that has now trampled the land. And when the popular minister demanded that justice be speeded out to the men who slew this officer while in the line of duty, silent promises must have gone up from the hearts of his hearers that law and order shall henceforth prevail and violators be punished. The choir at the First Baptist Church furnished the music at the home as well as the grave.

The casket was borne from the house to the hearse between two lines of his comrades composed of all the deputies of the county, all the courthouse officers and lawyers of the city, and a distinguished list of pallbearers. Among these pallbearers were: High Sheriff N.H. McGeachy; N.A. Watson, ex-Sheriff; W.C. Holland, Office Deputy; W.O. Patrick Deputy Sheriff; W.P West, Jailer; J.P. Kelly, Deputy Sheriff; J.H. Benton, Deputy Sheriff; W.W. Benderman; Deputy Sheriff; H.J. Hall, Deputy Sheriff; N.A. McLean, Deputy Sheriff; F.L. Holcomb, Deputy Sheriff; C.H. Randall, Deputy Sheriff; D.A. Wheeler, Deputy Sheriff; W.E. Honeycutt, Deputy Sheriff; Charles Driver, Deputy Sheriff; J.E. Marin; A.E. McLean; Arthur Schull; Carl Godwin; R.P. Fisher; Dave Gaster; all of which were Deputy Sheriffs except for the last was treasurer. Other pallbearers were: W.M. Walker, Clerk of Court; Merchison Walker, Deputy Clerk of Court; J.T. Martin, Chairman of the Board of Commissioners; H.L. Brothers, Attorney; W.W. Cook, Attorney; H.S. Abbrick, Attorney; V.C. Bullard, Attorney; W.C. Downey, Attorney. The active pallbearers were: John A. Oates, Gaper M. Scott, M.A. McLean, W.M. [not legible], John Owens, and Tom McQueen.

The floral tributes were immense and handsome and large baskets came from those who had labored with him in the courthouse, from friends, and one handsome bunch of flowers furnished from public subscription among the men on the streets. They all held Al Pate in the highest esteem and his death was a shock to the community. The body was carried from the home to Gee Burial Grounds to the rear of the Confederate Widow's Home where the interment took place.

After conducting the services inside the house, Rev. J. Snyder stepped out onto the porch and addressed the large crowd in the yard. 'It is my custom to say only a few words at funerals but this occasion calls for further remarks from me, my fellow citizens, for it is time that demands that every man search his own heart and find out where stands. A faithful officer has been shot down in the line of duty by an assassin who was violating the laws of the great land, laws that the majority of the people say shall be observed. This officer, who for twenty years or more has faithfully observed the duty and call of his chief, and went to his death because a man was openly violating the law. We must Christianize our land, drive out darkness and chaos, and make it safe for every man to live in peace. If this man had been a Christian, then Al Pate would have been alive today. You say, I believe ministers should preach forgiveness for this man who took this officer's life because the Lord preached forgiveness and repentance, and I reply by saying that should this man come to the courthouse, fall down upon his knees, and weepingly confess that he did this deed, and beg forgiveness, and if I had the positive assurance that he would live to correct his life ever after, I would say forgive him and let him go home to his family. But after not having this assurance I would say carry him into the courthouse and try him fairly and then punish him according to the law of the land. And if I were a lawyer I would not lend my influence, nor go into court and defend this assassin who took the life of a faithful officer when he was fulfilling his duty. We must make this land safe, not for our officers, but for every man, and the only way to do this is to put Christ into the hearts of men everywhere.' "

In the same issue of the *Fayetteville Observer*, a headline on the same page reads: "BAPTIST MINISTER RAPS LAW FOR LOWERING ETHICS. In his sermon Sunday, Reverend J.S. Snyder pays his respects to attorneys who take cases of unworthy clients. Reigns of lawlessness told." This article covers many columns in the *Fayetteville Observer* and is parallel with that concerning the slaying of Deputy Al J. Pate. An editorial from the same newspaper follows.

Fayetteville Observer
Fayetteville, North Carolina   July 25, 1921
Editorial:
CRIME IN CUMBERLAND COUNTY

Sheriff McGeachy severely censured the people of Godwin section shortly after the slaying of Deputy Sheriff Al J. Pate, supposedly by a violater of the prohibition law. Referring to the fact that while they could not but know that an illicit whiskey still was being operated just outside of town, apparently they took no action in the matter. And when he went there to rid them of the nuisance and to stop the violation of the law, one of his brave and faithful officers was murdered by an assassin in ambush.

Who can blame the Sheriff for his words of censure, or who will dare say that he is not performing his plain duty in urging citizens to inform him of the violation? Sheriff McGeachy is to be commended for his course. It is an alarming fact that the killing of officers for attempting to enforce the law in Cumberland County has got to be almost a common occurrence and the officers literally take their lives in their hands when they go forth in the performance of their duties. Why is this? The people of Cumberland, as a class, are as peaceful and law abiding as people of any other county of the state. Can it be that the attitude of the citizenship is responsible? Can it be that implied, if not expressed, sympathy with law violators has embodied the latter to resent the laws in appearance, and thus to resort to murder? It is to be devoutly hoped that such is not the case. There is something radically wrong and steps should be taken to get at the root of the trouble.

Without attempting even to defend or condemn prohibition, we wish to call attention to a common error in 'blaming prohibition.' Four deputies have been killed in Cumberland County within a twelve-month period while in performance of their duties. While prohibition law is held responsible by many for the whole catalog of crime, in fact, only one officer, Mr. Pate, was endeavoring to enforce that law. Deputies Moore and Butler were slain while pursuing Hobbs, who was not charged with either distilling or the sale of liquor. Deputy Blue was killed by Clayton on whom he was serving a peace warrant.

It is not the law that produces crime, but the contempt for and the rebellion against the law that are responsible. It is wrong and dangerous for otherwise good and sensible men to be proclaiming abroad that the passing of the act and the attempt to enforce it result in murder and lawbreaking. And he who spreads such doctrine is himself responsible in part for the bad state of affairs. Fayetteville and Cumberland County are confronted with a condition, not a theory. Murder of officers of the law can be stopped, but not by discussing theories as the cause of the crime, but by actual and earnest cooperation with the Sheriff in his efforts to bring criminals to justice and then to punish them.

A review of the *Fayetteville Observer* in July of 1921 reveals on every page in every account of the Pate slaying headlines reflecting violence, death, murder, whiskey traffic and a general crime wave that existed in this and other parts of the country.

CHAPTER 5
Trial and Conviction

Only once during countless interviews with members of the Williams family did I find a circumstance where details of a situation were forgotten or hazy. This was during my interviews with Miss Maggie concerning details of Marshall Williams' trial. While she remembered the dates well, many details of the grueling trial had long since escaped her memory. Obviously, that period was embarrassing and resulted in intense physical and mental strain on the defendant's wife.

"Marsh's first trial came up in November [1921]," Miss Maggie recalled. "Marsh's brother Mack was a lawyer and was living out West at the time, but he came home to help with the trials. [Marsh's] father hired several lawyers to work with Mack and, in fact, mortgaged a great part of the land to fund the needed legal counsel to try and save his son. It was here, Ross, that I believe God took a great hand in preserving Marsh's life so that he could create the things that were intended for him to do.

"When it came time for the jury to go out to come up with a verdict," Miss Maggie continued, "all but one person was determined that Marsh Williams should be executed. One man adamantly hung the jury. And finally an agreement was reached that if he would plead guilty to second-degree murder that the judge would direct the verdict, in lieu of an execution. This was so done and the court ordered that David Marshall Williams was sentenced to thirty years at hard labor and to wear a felon's stripes. As you know, Marsh served, as he put it, 'ten Christmases' [actually eight years] in prison."

Until April 11, 1976, some important facts concerning the activities of the night before the trial remained untold. Marsh's brothers Gordon and Leon Williams furnished the details:

"Ross, once as a small child, while playing in the field near the house, I was digging around like all farm kids do when suddenly I unearthed some empty cartridges," Gordon began. "They were Newton .30s and Krag .30 calibers. Excited about finding this 'treasure,' I dashed to the house to show Ma what I had found. To my bewilderment, Ma went to pieces; anger, fear and tears flashed in her eyes. She went immediately to the field and gathered up the rest of my find and returned to the house. I had no idea at that time that she and Leon, at midnight before the trial, had buried these cartridges and, more importantly, they had also buried Marsh's Krag rifle nearby, wrapped in a white sheet."

At this point Leon interrupted and revealed: "Ma and I went out way after midnight by lantern and began digging a hole in which we could bury that important Krag rifle and the cartridges. While doing so, some kind of a bug zoomed over our heads and Ma, being terribly scared and upset, exclaimed, 'Leon, was that a bullet whizzing over our heads?' We were not hiding the rifle because we felt that Marsh had done the killing, but we would have done almost anything to save his life."

"This was the rifle Marsh used at the still during that terrible shooting—the important one," Gordon added. "Some years later, at a time unknown to me, someone in the family went to the field and dug up his Krag. Ma instructed my brother Shell to take this rifle out to the barn loft and clean it and oil it. I saw it as he unwrapped it. It was in a stained, rotting white sheet, and as he unwrapped it, the sheet became whiter and whiter. There was Marsh's rifle, covered in heavy grease but with some parts rusting.

"I still remember that sound as Shell operated the bolt," Gordon continued. "There is nothing that sounds like a Krag when you open the bolt." Years later, Marsh cut the end of the barrel off because it was so badly rusted at that point." Mrs. Claud Williams, in a letter to Marshall dated December 8, 1926, while he was in prison, also *guardedly* referred to "your rifle"—(the Krag).

"It is my belief," Gordon said, "that the Newton [Marsh's other rifle] was left in the custody of Columbus McLellan, my brother-in-law.

"This Krag is believed still to be in the area." Neither rifle was introduced in court.

With an inflamed public pressing for an indictment for the murder of Deputy Sheriff Al Pate, the Williams family stood solidly behind Marshall Williams and carefully and prayerfully prepared for the day on which he would face Judge James C. McRae on murder charges. The reality was ever present that Marshall Willaims could if convicted, pay with his life for the fatal shooting of Deputy Pate.

The *Fayetteville Observer* assigned a reporter to follow the proceedings of the trial and wrote vigorously concerning each new development.

Fayetteville Observer
Fayetteville, North Carolina   August 1, 1921
MARSHALL WILLIAMS FACES JUDGE McRAE
TUESDAY ON CHARGE OF KILLING PATE

Preliminary hearing is planned for tomorrow morning of Godwin man. Strong lineup of lawyers on each side forecast bitter struggle for his life. Marshall Williams, of near Godwin, is expected to face the court of James C. McRae tomorrow morning for his preliminary hearing on the charge of the shooting to death of Deputy Sheriff Al J. Pate. If he is bound over, he will probably be tried at the coming criminal term of Cumberland Superior Court before Judge J.H. Kerr, presiding. The attorneys of the case are lined up as following: for the prosecution, Solicitor S.B. McLean, Sinclair & Dye, W.C. Downing, H.L. Brothers, and H.L.

Cook; for the defense, Stringfield & Bullard and Clifford & Townsend. The latter firm is from Dunn and one of the strongest in this section. L.R. Varser of Lumberton may also appear for the defense.

The attorneys for the prosecution are confident of binding over Williams at tomorrow's hearing and they are also confident of convicting him before the Superior Court. On the other hand, attorneys for the defense are banking on two or three theories to save their client. It is understood they will attempt to prove Williams was not in the neighborhood on the night Al Pate was killed and the fact that there is some testimony on the mother's side of the family will be a line of defense also, it is understood. There is very strong talk of the removal of the trial to another county, but whether the defense succeeds on this score remains with Judge Kerr when the matter comes before him the latter part of this month.

The prosecution will present a dozen witnesses, more or less, that they believe will lay around the defendant such a chain of testimony that he will be unable to break away from it. While there has been some feeling in the death of the popular and faithful officer, with sermons from the pulpit of First Baptist and First Presbyterian churches and a big mass meeting in the interest of law and order in Cumberland County, it is not believed sentiment has reached the point that Williams cannot get his fair trial here as elsewhere and the prosecution will fight removal to any other county with vigor. There were no eye witnesses to the actual shooting of Pate and both sides will depend upon circumstantial evidence, each side claiming it has some very strong and convincing testimony. However, what the testimony will disclose will be revealed when witnesses are called before Recorder McRae tomorrow morning. Based on this deadline, the arraignment will be on August 2, 1921.

It was the ruling of the court that Marshall Williams was to be held without bond for the death of Deputy Sheriff Al Pate. Again the *Fayetteville Observer* carefully reported the details of this eventful day.

Fayetteville Observer
Fayetteville, North Carolina   August 2, 1921

MARSHALL WILLIAMS IS HELD WITHOUT BOND FOR THE DEATH OF DEPUTY SHERIFF PATE AFTER LONG HEARING HERE TODAY. WILL FACE TWELVE JURORS IN SUPERIOR COURT SOON.

Five Negroes who were at the still operating it with Williams when raid took place testify they were given guns and told to shoot. Dawson said Williams told him he did shooting. Marshall Williams was just after twelve o'clock today bound over to the criminal term of the Cumberland Superior Court where he will face twelve jurors in the charge of murder of Deputy Sheriff Al J. Pate and be tried for his life. Judge McRae remanded him to the jail without bond after a lengthy hearing today in which the state weaved a net of evidence about him that those who heard it cannot imagine his escaping.

Under the direction of attorneys Robert H. Dye, N.A. Sinclair, Carl Downing, Henry L. Cook, H.L. Brothers, and Solicitor J.O. Talley, five witnesses went on the stand and told in the minutest detail the operation of the still on the afternoon of the raid that resulted in the shooting of Al Pate while he was sitting in his automobile, loaded down with the still, jugs, worm and all other paraphernalia coming down from Williams's plant. Old man Bob Godwin, his two sons, Neil and Aubrey, Frank Smith, and Randall Dawson, all colored, told the courts they had been employed by Marshall Williams to help him to operate that afternoon and he gave them all guns, saying, 'If the officers come, kill them with these.'

Deputy Sheriff C.H. Driver's testimony kills the effort of the defense to lay the actual shooting to Dawson. Mr. Driver swore he was walking behind the car when the shooting began, and as one bullet passed so close to his ear as to burn it, he saw Al Pate drop over on his face and he turned to see where the shots were coming from. He saw standing in the edge of the bushes a white man with his rifle to his shoulder. While he did not know Marshall Williams, he was asked by Attorney Carl Downing to point out the man who did the shooting and the Deputy pointed to Williams saying, 'To the best of my belief that is the man who shot the rifle.' Sheriff McGeachy was the first witness and he related in detail the raid and of seeing three men at the still, but could not identify either. He told of tearing up the plant, turning over the beer, loading up the car and starting away. He was walking in front of the car when the shooting began and he dropped to the ground. He then went around to the side of the car and found Deputy Pate had been killed instantly. The ball had entered his body just above the right hip, passed through his body, coming out through the left breast.

Randall Dawson, one of the Negroes at the still, was one of the first of them to be called to the witness stand and immediately the lawyers for the defense set up a howl about his testifying because he is also under indictment for helping to kill Pate, also for making liquor. Attorney Bullard presumed he was attorney for Dawson and wanted to instruct him not to testify if it incriminated himself. Attorney John G. Shaw occupied much of the court's time, making several arguments against making Dawson's testimony. He was told he need not tell anything that will be incriminating to himself and he proved an unwilling witness for a time. But suddenly he said, 'Well, here comes the whole thing, the truth as certain as Jesus died.' And he then told of seeing Marshall Williams along the road that afternoon with his rifle on his shoulder. They separated and he went home. Later on that night, Williams came to his house and talked with him about the breaking up of the still and the shooting of Pate. He said Williams told him, 'I did some shooting but I don't believe I hurt anyone. Yes, I did the shooting and meant to kill.' He saw Williams again Saturday morning and he still had his rifle with him. Dawson hooked up with Attorney Shaw who cross-examined him and the two matched wits for some time, the Negro leaving the stand having about held his own under the fire of the lawyers.

Uncle Bob Godwin, his two sons, Neil and Aubrey, and Frank Smith, all Negroes, testified that they were employed by Williams to help operate the still and were given rifles with instructions to shoot any officers who came in, but on the appearance of the Sheriff's party they all fled. They all said Williams had his high-powered rifle with him and carried it off when he left the still. They all told of hearing rifle shots after leaving the still, coming from the direction in which Williams fled.

Sheriff McGeachy was recalled to the stand and produced a shoe box containing steel-jacketed bullets from rifles, empty cartridges, pictures and a book containing the names of persons Williams had sold liquor to on credit. The lawyers rankled some time over the introduction of this box but they were put into evidence. The Sheriff said in Williams's house is a rack where he keeps his rifles and 'arsenal' is written on the wall. Also on the wall is a skeleton of a pistol and some skull and bones.

Randall Dawson, recalled, said he was at the still but fled just before the officers came into the woods. He was handed a gun by Williams and told to see that it was kept safe if the officers should come. He carried it home with him. Attorney Shaw fought hard to locate Dawson at the spot where the shooting took place but he made very little headway; and finally admitted himself in an argument with Dawson that he was not getting far. Three guns were identified in court as belonging to Williams. When the state announced that it was closed, the defense made the same announcement and without argument, Judge McRae bound Williams over without bond to Superior Court.

Marshall Williams stepped closer to the gallows as the jurors decreed that he, along with Randall Dawson, be indicted and held over for further investigation. The following news article gives an account of these proceedings.

Fayetteville Observer
Fayetteville, North Carolina   August 2, 1921
**CORONERS JURY INDICTS DAWSON
AND WILLIAMS**

Inquest held into death of Deputy Pate recommends that Marshall Williams and Randall Dawson both be held. County Coroner, Dr. R.A. Allgood, held an inquest Monday night on the killing on July 22 of Deputy Sheriff

A.J. Pate, which occurred while Deputy Pate was in discharge of the duty of enforcing the prohibition law near Godwin, this county. The jury rendered the following verdict: 'We the undersigned jury, after being duly sworn and hearing the evidence, do find the deceased, A.J. Pate, came to his death as the result of a bullet wound gun in hands and some party unknown to this jury. We recommend that one Marshall Williams and R.A. Dawson be held without bail for further investigation by the courts.' This was signed Fred D. Williams, R.L. Holland, Jr., F.L. Black, M.A. Bethune, N. Melton, R.L. Holland, Sr. This the first day of August, 1921.

Testimony given before the coroners jury is as follows: 'Sheriff N.H. McGeachy, Friday, July 22, at six-thirty p.m., went on to this still about one half mile east of Godwin station. We found the still in operation. I saw three men running away from the still. Mr. Pate and I were right in on it. George West and Charles Randall were behind me. We broke up the still, found three guns at the still, took the still and about thirty gallons of whiskey, cap and worm and carried them about forty steps to the edge of the field. I sent out to the road after the car, which was about one hundred and fifty yards from the road, loaded still and equipment on car and started toward the road. Mr. Pate got in car with George West, who was driving. I was walking in front of the car with Bill West and Charles Driver. When we were about one hundred yards from the woods going out toward the road leading to Falcon, and heard report of the rifle, I immediately looked back. I was about twenty feet in front of car and in about one minute's time, heard another report and George West jumped out of the car and Mr. Pate sat still in the car. He was killed with the first shot. There were some five or six shots fired. I ran back to the car. I could tell the direction from which the shots came. He was about forty or fifty yards from where we loaded the still. I picked up rifle. He stopped shooting about that time. Afterwards I searched Marshall Williams's house and found a box with four or five army rifle cartridges in it similar to the ones found in the army rifle which was found at the still. I searched his house once before and found an army rifle, but longer gauge. I did not find any guns at the time I searched his house after shooting. His wife said that he had been gone about one half hour. I could not recognize anyone in the woods and could not recognize the man who was doing the shooting. I told his wife to tell him to come and give himself up, that we were looking for him. She said that she would use her influence for me. The shooting happened about sundown.' This was signed N.H. McGeachy.

R.A. Dawson: 'I saw Marshall Williams this morning after Mr. Pate was killed. He was on the road coming from his daddy's and was near my house. This about six a.m. He had one rifle and one breech loader that shoots five times. He left the breech-loading gun with me. I think there were two or three shells in it. I had bothered him to buy a gun some time before, six or eight weeks ago. I broke mine. I borrowed the gun this morning that he left with me. I did not say anything to him about what had happened the day before. He said that he had heard that they had captured or gotten everything. I told him that one of the officers was killed. He said, 'I done some shooting,' but he was not anywhere about. He left me and went toward home. It was his long rifle that he had with him that morning, his long rifle with a leather strap on it. I did not see Williams the evening before. Marshall Williams told me that there was a still in the woods and invited me in. I went in twice. The first time I went in he was there. There was a pump and some barrels there. He said he was going to make some whiskey there. The second time I went in the still was hot. Saw lots of barrels and two men stooping down. I asked where the boss man was. Marshall Williams was supposed to be the boss. They said that he was not there. I went through Friday evening about five o'clock. I went by the still to get a drink of whiskey. I did not know who the men were at the still. Marshall came by my house about six a.m. and left the gun with me. Said keep it until he called for it and that they had captured everything he had. And I told him that I heard some bad news. He hung his head down and said that he did some shooting but did not think he did any harm.' Signed R.A. Dawson.

Marshall Williams, known to be a wild young man, continuously in trouble, was confined in the Raeford County

Jail — confined to a cell with little to do but to review mentally the recent court events and to face the reality that he might well be sentenced to be hanged if convicted of the murder of Deputy Al Pate.

An attempted jail break took place at the Raeford County Jail while Williams was confined there. However, he had given his word he would not try to escape and, when the opportunity presented itself, was willing to remain confined, even if it was to cost him his life later on in the courtroom. The following newspaper account give details of the attempted break.

Fayetteville Observer
Fayetteville, North Carolina   August 11, 1921
ATTEMPTED JAIL BREAK AT RAEFORD

Jailer N.A. Watson sandbagged by three prisoners who failed to effect a getaway, one of them sent to Hoke from this county.

A sandbagged jailer and an unsuccessful attempt to break jail at Raeford last night was the story told the 'Observer' over the telephone wires by Sheriff Hall of Hoke County this morning. Three prisoners attacked Jailer N.A. Watson and sandbagged him, but the jail was so secure that the officer recovered sufficiently to call for assistance before they could effect escape. One of the prisoners, Elsa Hall of Hoke Mills, has been sent to Hoke from this county for safekeeping, being bound over by Superior Court on charges of carrying concealed weapons and store-breaking. Two other prisoners were Hoke County prisoners.

Carbine recalled vividly the events of the attempted jail break at the Raeford County jail.

"Ross, there seemed to be no end of excitement," he began. "When I was in the Raeford jail, I wasn't there long before there was an attempted jail break. There was several fellers in there that had accumulated bottles and beat them up and put them into socks, making blackjacks out of them. When the jailer opened the door and they let him in, they jumped on him and they beat the plumb hell out of him. And he had on a white shirt and blood was running down on it from his face. It was shortly thereafter that these prisoners locked him up in the cell, after I insisted that they stop beating him.

"They got out of the cell and this fellow, Watson, who was leading the attempted break, had the keys on him," Carbine continued. "He was asking me to hand him his knife or something. He couldn't get out of the outer section of the jail. The escapees asked me if I was going with them and I told them I wasn't going anywhere, because I had given my word that I wouldn't try and escape. The prisoners couldn't get out and the overall escape was a failure. They were later taken to trial at the court in Raeford.

"The judge asked these boys if Williams tried to escape and they said No. One of them made some kind of comment that I must not be guilty because I didn't try to go with them."

Toward the end of August and continuing into September, preparations proceeded for Cumberland County's trial of the century. A special term of court was scheduled for October, at which time Williams' case was to be tried.

Fayetteville Observer
Fayetteville, North Carolina   August 27, 1921
ONE OF THE BIGGEST DOCKETS IN COUNTY'S HISTORY TO FACE JUDGE JOHN H. KERR

Criminal Court will be in session here next week with Marshall Williams's case holding greatest interest. Great legal battle in store in this case. One of the largest criminal dockets in the history of Cumberland County will face Judge John H. Kerr when Cumberland County Superior Court begins on Monday morning for a one week term. Some seventy-five cases are on docket.

The biggest case of the public interest to be tried is that against Marshall Williams of Godwin who will face twelve of his countrymen on the charge of taking the life of Deputy Sheriff Al J. Pate while a sheriff's party was raiding a still alleged to have been the property of Williams. One of the strongest groups of legal talent in this section ever to be displayed will be in court for this trial.

Fayetteville Observer
Fayetteville, North Carolina   August 29,1921
JUDGE KERR DELIVERS MOST REMARKABLE CHARGE TO JURY. WARNS VIOLATORS OF LAW IN IMPRESSIVE DELIVERY. STRONG JURY IS CHOSEN TO SERVE FOR SIX MONTHS.

His Honor at great length pled with citizens to strive for human efficiency, the three great attributes of which are: education, health and morals. It's interesting to note the grand jurors for that period. The following were named as members of the grand jury to serve for a period of six months: Gilbert C. Trice, foreman, Charles Rankin, Charles D. Hutaff, I. H. Bullard, J. J. Hair, Fred C. Owens, Leon Averitt, J. McBain, D. V. Cannady, Emmitt Covington, G. C. Harper, J. L. Horne, R. D. Fisher, A. D. Cashwell, T. W. Hair, J. C. Williams, Jr., C. P. Britt. The narration was received with applause by the people in the courtroom.

Judge Kerr rushes court speedily along, three cases being called before him. This is on August 30, 1921, an effort being made to remove from the court lesser cases.

Fayetteville Observer
Fayetteville, North Carolina   August 31, 1921

Yesterday afternoon Marshall Williams, alleged slayer of Deputy Sheriff Al J. Pate, was arraigned and the case continued for the rest of the term. It is understood that a special term of court will be held in the first or second week of October and this case will be taken up and tried at this time. Attorneys Clifford & Townsend of Dunn were present with the local attorneys representing Williams yesterday.

Fayetteville Observer
Fayetteville, North Carolina   September 1, 1921

His Honor held open for further consideration the case of Marshall Williams. Attorney Downey for the State made the greatest speech that has yet been made before the jury here. 'The best way to teach a man insanity is to follow his acts through life,' he said and proceeded to enumerate his unwillingness to work when a youth, his marriage, providing for his wife, work on the railroad, county roads, and else, made his own trade, did his own business, went off to school at a military school, where he violated the rules and was dismissed, then placed on a train to come home by himself, went to school with other boys and kept up with them in his work, secured a whiskey still and placed it in the very best place near the town of Godwin to carry out his traffic. Great speech!

'If his father had determined like Mr. Charlie Spell to conquer him in his youth and make him recognize authority, he would not this morning be sitting here, charged with the murder of Al J. Pate. He would be back in Godwin attending to his lawful business. Insanity? It will be only a matter of time when they will have the experts in Virginia to say he has recovered. Then when Driver and Dawson have passed out of the jurisdiction of this court, they will ask twelve true men whether he took the life of Al Pate.

'A short time ago I saw two mangled bodies of true soldiers killed overseas, men who died that other men may live, laid to rest at Cedar Creek. Then later on, I followed a coffin to a little graveyard back of the Widow's Home and there the remains of Al Pate was lowered into the grave and, I tell you today, Al Pate died that we might live. He died a hero just as much as those who died on the battlefield in Europe. Al Pate may soon be forgotten, but the principles he stood for will live forever—the principles of law and order.'

Attorneys Q. K. Nimocks for the defense, N. A. Sinclair for the State, and J. G. Schoff for the defense spoke in that order, followed by the charge of Judge Kerr.

At a meeting of the Williams family, it was decided that no thread of evidence could be withheld nor could any bit of information be held back, regardless of embarrassment that it might cause the family. Marshall Williams' life must be saved.

A letter written on October 29, 1919, by the Reverend J. M. "Mack" Williams, half brother of Marshall Williams, was turned over to the defense attorneys. The Reverend Williams' letter, written to another brother, John Williams, cautioned that Marshall, in his opinion, suffered from paranoia. He expressed deep concern that Marshall, as he grew older, might actually kill those closest to him. The following is a copy of the letter:

October 29, 1919

Dear John,

    I thought of writing you last Sunday but did not. I have been studying up at odd times about Marshall. He has what is called paranoia. I have talked to several men who were in a position to know. People with the above disease almost invariably get worse. I read a number of books on it while I was in Psychological Division of the Army and since being here. He will get worse the older he gets. Now anyone with paranoia almost always attacks the one closest to him. He seems to have a particular grudge against his father and against his wife. The history of such cases is that the first person they kill they go mad and try to kill everybody. He certainly had paralysis of nerves of the head while I was down there and was very much worse Sunday than he was two or three days later. He has an insane delusion of being a bandit and killing someone. And if he is not restrained in some way the result in the next two or three years can almost be predicted. I would not go down there and live with him a month for any amount of money. I have gone over in my mind since leaving there every element in the case. The minute I spoke to him I knew what was the matter and everything I have seen since has only confirmed what I first thought. I write this not because I want to, but because it is my belief that I give it to you for what it is worth.

        Your brother,
        Mac
        109 East Broadway
        Louisville, Kentucky

On October 17, 1921, a mistrial in the Williams case was declared when the jurors could not reach a verdict.

This opened the possibility that Williams might be retried on the lesser charge of second-degree murder.

In recalling events of that day, Carbine's wife expressed gratitude that her husband's life was spared. "Ross, I will always believe that it was God's will that Marsh's life was spared. I gave thanks when I learned that the clerk had declared a mistrial. It was not intended that Marsh was to die on the gallows."

The *Fayetteville Observer,* still following the trail closely, gave the following account of the day's events.

Fayetteville Observer
Fayetteville, North Carolina   October 17, 1921
JURY DISAGREES, CLERK DECLARES MISTRIAL TODAY. AFTER BEING OUT FORTY-FIVE HOURS, MARSHALL WILLIAMS JURY REPORTS DIS-AGREEMENT.

Say court stood 11 to 1 for sanity. Lawyers say both sides may consent to trial for murder in the second degree. After considering and arguing the case for the forty-five hours, the jury on the Marshall Williams's insanity issue announced at ten o'clock today, Monday, to Clerk of the Court W. M. Walker, that they could not agree, whereupon the clerk withdrew a juror and declared it a mistrial. It is said that from the beginning the jury stood 11 for sanity and one for insanity and no amount of argument or persuasion could convert the one man over to the side of the eleven. Whether this failure of the jury to agree will result in another trial of the insanity issue, legal authorities are not prepared to state, as it is possible that both sides may consent to a trial of murder in the second degree.

The one week term of Cumberland Superior Court which convened here Monday on the tenth inst. came to a close Saturday afternoon. The trial issue of the sanity or insanity of Marshall Williams in connection with the killing of Deputy Sheriff A. J. Pate last July occupied practically the entire week, it coming on to be heard at one o'clock Tuesday afternoon. The evidence and arguments of counsel were completed at one o'clock Saturday afternoon when the case went to jury. The jury being unable to agree was held together and a stubborn jury it proved to be. At ten o'clock this morning, after having had forty-five hours to study the case, the jurors were still unable to agree and Clerk of the Court W. M. Walker declared a mistrial.

Judge John H. Kerr, who presided over the court, left here Saturday afternoon for his home, leaving the case in the hands of the Clerk of the Court. Judge Kerr asked the jurors before leaving if they wished any instructions or information on points of the law and they replied that they did not. The Judge passed through Fayetteville this morning on the way to Elizabethtown to hold court and instructed the clerk to dismiss the jury whenever he saw fit, if he was satisfied that they could not agree.

Following the mistrial, attorneys on both sides were busy with daily meetings, discussions and negotiations. On November 19, 1921, the *Fayetteville Observer,* maintaining its vigilance, announced that Marshall Williams' case would come up for a second trial. In the following days, headlines and special bulletins covered the front page and spotlighted this historic Cumberland County trial.

Fayetteville Observer
Fayetteville, North Carolina   November 19, 1921
CRIMINAL TERM OF SUPERIOR COURT TO OPEN MONDAY. MARSHALL WILLIAMS'S CASE WILL COME UP FOR SECOND TIME HERE NEXT WEEK.

A one-week term of Cumberland Superior Court for the trial of criminal cases will convene Monday with Judge Henry P. Lane, presiding, and Solicitor S. B. McLean representing the State. Judge J. H. Kerr was to have presided, it being his last term here for some time, but he exchanged placed with Judge Lane. At this term the capital case of Marshall Williams for the alleged killing of Deputy Sheriff A. J. Pate was to come up for the second time. It will be remembered that Williams was tried on an insanity issue some weeks ago but the jury failed to agree standing eleven to one for insanity. The docket for this term is a full one, there being some seventy-five cases for trial.

Fayetteville Observer
Fayetteville, North Carolina   November 21, 1921

WILLIAMS WILL BE BROUGHT TO CITY TOMORROW. COUNSEL FOR THE DEFENSE AND SOLICITOR FAILED TO AGREE AT CONFERENCE TODAY.

Criminal term of court opens today. Marshall Williams's case is the only important one to come up at this time.

BULLETIN

In Superior Court here today, when Solicitor S. B. McLean called the case of Marshall Williams charged with the killing of Deputy Sheriff A. J. Pate, John G. Shaw for the defense stated that the counsel wished to hold a conference on the matter.

The conference was held. When Mr. Shaw announced that counsel for the defense and for the State could not agree and that they wished to have the prisoner Williams brought into the court from Raeford jail where he is confined, the Solicitor consented and Williams will appear in court tomorrow morning.

A one-week term of Cumberland Superior Court for the trial of criminal cases only convened here today with Judge Henry P. Lane on the bench and Solicitor S. B. McLean prosecuting. The Judge stated that he would not charge the grand jury, as it has been drawn for six months and already had been charged. But he added that he would give the jury any information they wanted in any matter coming before them.

The docket had about eighty cases but none of special importance except that of Marshall Williams charged with the murder of Deputy Sheriff Al Pate. Pate was shot and killed several months ago while assisting in the capture of a blockade liquor still at Godwin in this county, alleged to belong to Williams. The still had been dislodged and placed in the car for transportation to Fayetteville. Pate was sitting in the automobile and the posse was preparing to leave the location where the still was found, when he was shot from ambush. He died almost instantly. Williams gave himself up a day or two after the killing and after a sheriff's posse had searched in vain for him.

He was tried at a special term of court in October. He pleaded insanity and the case was tried on that issue. Alienists and Williams's father and relatives and other citizens testified but the jury failed to agree, eleven being for sanity and one being for insanity. The case will be tried again at this term of court, but whether or not on the insanity issue is not known. Case of minor importance to be tried this afternoon.

On November 22, 1921, the town was shocked to learn that Marshall Williams had pleaded guilty to second-degree murder.

Fayetteville Observer
Fayetteville, North Carolina   November 22,1921
WILLIAMS PLEADS GUILTY TO MURDER IN THE SECOND DEGREE.

Surprise is sprung in Marshall Williams's case late this afternoon. Judge will pass sentence Friday. He is to read over the transcript evidence and to pass sentence next Friday.

BULLETIN

After the midday recess of the Superior Court today, counsel for the defense in the case of Marshall Williams, charged with the murder of Deputy Sheriff Al J. Pate, withdrew the plea of insanity from which Williams was tried during the October term of court and on which the jury failed to agree, and entered the plea of not guilty as to the charge of murder in the first degree but a plea of guilty to a charge of murder in the second degree. The counsel for the defense suggested that the Judge read the typewritten evidence, which he consented to do, and will pass sentence next Friday. The State consented to the plea of murder in second degree. This move by the defense came as a surprise in the case which has aroused interest in the entire State of North Carolina.

Marshall Williams is charged with the murder of Deputy Sheriff Al Pate. The murder took place July 22, 1921. On account of the unsafe conditions of the Cumberland County jail, Williams was taken to Raeford and lodged in the Hoke County jail there. In October a special term of Cumberland Superior Court was called for the trial, at which time he entered a plea of insanity. A great array of witnesses testified both for State and the defense. Aliens of note and relatives and friends testified for the defense and aliens and neighbors of the prisoner testified for the State. The trial consumed nearly a week and the jury remained out about thirty-six hours, [it was actually forty-five hours] standing eleven to one for sanity. Williams is prominent in the county, his father being at one time Chairman of the County Commissioners. According to lawyers this afternoon, the minimum sentence that can be given upon the charge of the defendant guilty is ten years and the maximum is thirty.

Miss Maggie recalled the agony of the realization that her husband was to be incarcerated. At the same time she expressed thankfulness that his life was spared: "Marsh was to be taken away from me — given thirty years at hard labor and wear a felon's stripes. It was hard, but I could not help but be thankful that God had chosen to spare his life. Only one day lapsed between the time Marsh was sentenced and the time he was driven to the State Prison. I intended to wait for him."

The *Fayetteville Observer* headlined both his conviction and his departure for prison:

Fayetteville Observer
Fayetteville, North Carolina   November 25, 1921
EXTRA! MARSHALL WILLIAMS WAS LATE
TODAY GIVEN THE MAXIMUM SENTENCE OF
THIRTY YEARS FOR THE MURDER OF DEPUTY
SHERIFF A.J. PATE.

Fayetteville Observer
Fayetteville, North Carolina   November 26, 1921
BIDS FAREWELL TO MOTHER AND WIFE ON
WAY TO PRISON. SHERIFF TAKES MARSHALL
WILLIAMS TO PRISON TO BEGIN LONG
SENTENCE. FATHER GOES WITH SHERIFF AND
SON. WILLIAMS TESTIFIES DURING TRIAL OF
NEGRO FOLLOWING HIS SENTENCE.

At about ten-fifteen o'clock this morning, Sheriff N.H. McGeachy took Marshall Williams to the State Prison at

Raleigh to begin serving his thirty year sentence for second degree murder in the killing of Deputy Sheriff A.J. Pate last July. Claud Williams, father of the prisoner, accompanied the Sheriff and his son. The Sheriff and his party went through the country in automobiles. They went by the prisoner's home at the Black River Township in order that he might bid farewell to his wife and mother. Mr. Williams, the father, went to the State Prison with his son after the leavetaking at the Williams's home

In getting through as much of the docket as possible before the adjournment of the Cumberland County Superior Court, Judge Lane disposed of the following cases: Frank Henchmen, larceny, guilty, twelve months; Will Jackson, housebreaking; Ham Dawson, charged with secret assault on Deputy Sheriff A.J. Pate at the time when Pate was killed last July on the raid of Marshall Williams's still, not guilty. In this case Williams went on the stand and testified that on the night Pate was killed, he, Williams, fired one time. He did not shoot to kill and that when he shot to kill, he always hit his mark. He further testified that Dawson fired four times. Dawson asked Williams if he shot to kill and Williams replied that he did not. Then Williams asked Dawson if he shot to kill and Dawson said that he did. Williams said that he wanted to give this testimony because Dawson had gone back on him.

Superior Court: The criminal term of court here adjourns. Superior Court for the trial of criminal cases, which was held here during this week with Judge H.P. Lane presiding, adjourned last night and the Judge and Solicitor S.B. McLean returned to their home state. With the exception of Marshall Williams's case, the cases before them were of minor importance.

CHAPTER 6
Prison Days

For a young man who had spent the majority of his life romping freely through the woods and wide open spaces, departure for prison would seem to be particularly traumatic. Yet Carbine showed no signs of shock or loss of memory as, years later, he graphically recalled preparation for, and arrival at, prison.

Departure for Prison

"After the trial," Carbine began, "Sheriff McGeachy came to Raeford with my father in a big-six Studebaker car with a cloth top. They were called then a touring car. My brother-in-law, named McClellan, was driving the Studebaker. The sheriff as he walked in said very casually, 'Marshall, is everything all right?' And I said, 'Everything is fine, sheriff,' or something like that. And we walked out together, got in the car, just like some people going to town. My brother Mack and Pa were in the car.

"We drove fifteen miles back to Godwin and we visited the old house here—just came by to say good-bye to the folks. And, of course, to say some final words to Ma and to Maggie. I remember that while we were talking the sheriff got out and walked around looking at the good mules and cows that Pa had around the house, and just wandered around while we talked. I went in the house and had a visit and the sheriff was nice enough to say, 'When you all get ready just come on out and get in the car and I'll know.' "

Other eyes focused on the arrival of Marshall Williams at the homeplace. Not certain of exactly what was happening, Gordon Williams, youngest brother of Marshall, watched as his convicted brother visited for a few precious minutes with his family. These same eyes viewed the departure of his brother, not fully understanding the gravity of the occasion.

The three brothers closest to Marshall Williams, Gordon, Shell and Leon, met with me on April 10, 1976, at Godwin and shared long-suppressed personal feelings concerning the days when Marshall Williams was imprisoned. Gordon not only shared his feelings but made available a number of personal letters written to Marsh both by him, as a child of ten to fifteen, and by his mother. Neither these letters nor these long-hidden emotions had ever before been shared with anyone. They bear evidence of the grief felt by the family over the incarceration of Marshall Williams.

"I was a small child, but there are two times I will never forget," Gordon began. "The first was that day when Marshall was brought by our home by the sheriff on the way to prison. You see, being so young, I had been shielded completely from the trial and from the news accounts, but I will never forget that day when he left for prison. The sheriff drove up in the yard to the grove in front of the house. He parked between the front yard gate and the hitching post. There were three gates: the front, side gate and back gate. Waiting to meet him was Ma and Maggie. I was waiting with them.

"If I remember correctly," he continued, "Pa drove out in the car with Marshall and the sheriff. The sheriff, after greeting the family, walked around outside and allowed Marshall time to visit with the family. Everyone held back their emotions during the visit in the living room. It was difficult, but everyone maintained their composure until that moment when Marshall, the sheriff and Pa drove down the road from the house and out that front gate. It was at that moment that our world collapsed . . . . Ross, no studio in Hollywood could have possibly captured the sorrow and emotion of that moment. It was so terrifying to me as a child, and so beyond my understanding, that I ran and crawled under the house. . . . It was here that, as I looked up and as I stared at the hand-hewn sills, that I had engraved in my heart and mind forever the prayers and sobbing of Ma and Maggie.

"Ross, his departure in my eyes was like a death in the family, for Marsh was my older brother and my hero. In my eyes it was worse than death for I knew that he was going to a living death. I guess maybe this explains why I devoted many hours during his stay in prison writing him letters, and drawing fun things in these letters. It was my way of sending a little happiness to Marshall. He never forgot this either. My letters tried to tell him everything that was at, or happening at, home. I told of my rabbit traps, possum hunting, the crops, my pigs, eating hickory nuts (and I saved and sent him some each fall), and tried in each letter, in my child-like way, to tell him that all was well at home.

"Marsh shed no tears when he left. He was cold, blue steel. [But] his return some years later was a different story," Gordon concluded.

Miss Maggie remembered equally as vividly the day Marshall Williams departed. Sitting on the little stool in her kitchen, and gazing intently across the backyard and open fields, she confided:

"Ross the most vivid mental picture that has stuck with me is the way that I felt on the fatal day when Marshall came by to tell us good-bye on the way to prison. After they left for Raleigh I remember that I went out into the backyard and, leaning against the old picket fence, I looked across the brown corn fields and I thought — 'thirty years is almost forever'. . . .

"I also thought I should not fade into oblivion. Remember, Ross, this was over a half century ago. Women just did not work outside the home. There were only two professions that were acceptable then. One, train for school

102

teaching. The other was going in the nursing field. I was blessed with a rare religious heritage that stood me in good stead all these years, and at that moment I felt it most. My mother had always wanted me and my sister to be school teachers so that day I decided I would train for teaching. I enrolled in what is now called East Carolina University and was a member of the 1926 graduating class. I taught first grade until Marsh came home and perhaps two or three years afterwards. Making a good life for oneself is so rewarding. To this day I am glad I made the choice to do just that."

The time came all too soon for Marshall Williams to end his good-byes to his family and to begin the journey to the State Prison.

"Time had come and we just went out and got in the car and headed for Raleigh," Marshall recalled. "If you had met us, you wouldn't have known anything out of the ordinary. I don't know exactly what kind of attitude I developed, but I was the kind of person that was almost indifferent to any kind of surroundings. So the Raleigh prison wasn't anything to me. It didn't throw me off too much."

Marshall Williams, twenty-one years old, sat in his father's Studebaker outside the big gate of North Carolina State Prison at Raleigh, looking over what he anticipated to be his home for the next thirty years. Not grasping in the least the hardships ahead of him, his only thought at the moment was: "Well, my new home is a big one, that's for sure."

Psychology Was a Leather Strap

Prisons in the early 1900's were not "departments of corrections" as we know and visualize them today. Their principal function was to confine those who had violated the law. Efforts to effect rehabilitation were almost unknown — especially for "cop killers," as convicts such as Williams were classified. "Psychology" came in the form of a perforated leather strap or leg irons. Survival was definitely for the fittest. Complete obedience to every

Photo 14. Following Williams' conviction for second-degree murder, he was sent to North Carolina State Prison in Raleigh to begin serving his thirty-year sentence. It was here that he vowed that someday he would make amends for the hurt caused his family.

command, regardless of the fairness of that command, was one's only assurance of "getting along," and this was to come hard to the young prisoner Marsh Williams (Photo 14).

Appendicitis

Williams had been in confinement less than two months when he suffered an attack of appendicitis. He recalled the trauma of the event:

"When I first started serving my 'long-term contract' with the State of North Carolina—the kind of contract you could not break—I had not been there long before I had a pain in my side. [This was in January of 1922.] One of the guards thought I was faking and punched me hard in my stomach. I fell to the ground and they must have realized I was sick for sure, for I didn't get up swinging. It turned out that I had one hellish attack of appendicitis. It ruptured. I got in pretty bad shape there. They had a good surgeon come out from Raleigh and he fixed me up. I stayed in the hospital for awhile but as soon as I was fairly well recovered, I was sent out to a place called Cary Prison Farm. [Although located on a rural route of the town of Cary,] it was located just a few miles out of Raleigh. The prison had gotten a lot of complaints from citizens about the goings-on out there at Cary. I think they just got tired of seeing the abuse of human beings and would rather it be done someplace else."

Transfer to Topton

An interview with Gordon Williams revealed an interesting episode involving Marsh while he was held at Cary Prison Farm—one which led to his transfer to Topton:

"Following his appendicitis operation," Gordon confided, "an unexpected examination of Marsh's bandages revealed a dagger carefully concealed under his bandages. This really upset prison officials, regardless of the fact that Marsh's dagger was not for use against officials but was, in reality, intended for protection from the abuses of other prisoners." This exposure resulted in Williams' being classified as a "hard case."

Happenings such as this, and other more serious disturbances, caused the North Carolina State Prison system to take still further action against those they considered dangerous or tough cases. Orders were issued that some of the prisoners were to be transferred to a place called Topton.

"In short order [in early 1922] they separated the white prisoners from the colored ones and they sent us to a place called Topton," Carbine recalled. "This transfer was effected by placing all of us that were going to Topton on a prison train. Now, Ross, you have never been on one of these trains, but I'll tell you that it was something. That train was loaded with people that were in for every conceivable crime. On the way a couple of them jumped out of the train windows, chains and all. They didn't stop the train — no sir — if they had stopped the train, they could have lost us all. There were between seventy-five and one hundred prisoners on board that special train.

"Ross, every man sent [to Topton] was a convicted murderer with from thirty years to life to serve," he continued. "It was a group of bad men for damn sure. Topton was located in the Blue Ridge Mountains of North Carolina. It was considered absolutely the worst prison in the country. It made Cary Prison Farm and others appear to be a country club."

Captain H.T. Peoples

It was not only the dire conditions which made Topton memorable for Carbine Williams. He met there a prison employee who would recognize and foster his mechanical genius.

"It was here, Ross, on arrival [at Topton, midway between Topton and Robbinsville, North Carolina], that I met for the first time a man that was later to become my very great friend — Captain H.T. Peoples," Carbine pointed out. "He had the reputation of being tough but fair. He had us lined up and I remember he said, 'You boys look

all right to me. I don't see anything wrong with you at all.'
He walked up to me and said, 'Son, why are you here?' He
asked you in such a way that you answered him.

"I tell you now that Topton was a hard rock camp,"
he emphasized. "No kidding! To begin with, we slept on
chains in cages. Every man had an iron cuff around his
ankle and each night you slipped a long 'gang chain'
through your cuff and passed it on to the next man and he
did the same. You slept in cages like animals. When one
man moved during his sleep the chain tugged every man
on the line.

"You were up before daylight and worked until dark
on road construction, breaking rock with sledge hammers
and rolling rock with your bare hands. The slightest violation of any rule and you were brought to a whipping stake.
Your hands were tied high on that stake and your shirt
removed. A guard then inflicted the designated number of
lashes with a wide leather whipping belt that was perforated all over. It was horrible to see and sickening to the
spirit. Many a night a punished man moaned through the
night next to you after receiving these lashes. It was here
that I decided that if I had to make the rest of my time
under these conditions that I would either escape or be
killed," Carbine revealed.

Trouble at Topton

"I had other difficulties once or twice," Carbine admitted. "It looked like something dangerous was brewing.
I stayed around the watering trough, in back of the barracks, waiting for another prisoner one time but he never
showed up. We knew that it was coming, kind of an
internal gang war. Me and about four boys, my henchmen,
you know, decided that the best place to escape to was the
Blue Ridge Mountains and wait there because somebody
was really gonna get hurt.

"It was kind of lucky for that man he didn't show up
at the watering trough. Yeah, he caught wind of it, I guess.
There was plenty of them around there that wouldn't have
known nothing if anything had happened to him. They

arranged to be there so nobody could see anything or hear anything or do anything. It would have been 'one of them things,' " Carbine said with a shrug.

"I was so disgusted, I never took a bath while I was there," Carbine continued. "That was the only place that I was figuring on escaping from. Me and about five or six more were going. . . . Nobody was going with us except killers, and they had to be in from twenty to thirty or life. Even then, you had to take a hard look at them to know whether you liked them and could trust them. Just about a week before we were going, word got out that we were going to Caledonia.

"In later years I told Captain Peoples about how we were gonna pull that escape off," Carbine said confidently. "The mountain roads were long and were mighty crooked. About fifty or sixty men in a column, they'd be spread out going around the curvy road and the guard foreman of the whole thing was walking up in the middle. The first thing we were gonna do was to take his pistol. And the man in front, God help him, because he couldn't shoot the foreman and couldn't shoot nobody in the middle because there were too many men in there behind the foreman. The man in front, before he knew what in the world was going on, he'd have a .38 special in his ass. He wouldn't even know it. And then, of course, we'd take his gun and that would be the whole show — we'd be out. It was as simple as that.

"The first thing, we were gonna take the gun off of the foreman," he continued. "I forgot his name. He finally went to Caledonia. You know, it didn't take but just a part of a second to do something like that, and the man in front wouldn't know anything because on that curvy road the guards couldn't hardly see each other. The roads were being built, you know. They were not straightened out, you know. They were working on them. You couldn't see either end. The guy on the front and the rear could hardly see each other at times. Before anybody knew it, one guard would be under control and you wouldn't even have to wait for the other. We could have just kept on going. You wouldn't even have to engage the guard behind."

"What did Captain Peoples say when you told him about this?" I asked.

"He had the flattest looking face I've ever seen," Carbine reflected. "His face looked as flat as a pancake. He said, 'I'm sure glad you didn't!' Boy, it had the flattest look! He wouldn't have been involved because he would have never been with us. He would have been at the camp.

"I remember we boys would go back and see the mountain cabins, you know, way down in the valley," Carbine reflected. "They were just waiting for you to come, 'cause them folks would look out for you. It weren't like a lot of places. They'd help you if you got there. We'd look at the blue smoke coming up there, you know, and how peaceful it was looking at them — oh brother!

"Now some of them [prisoners] were mountain boys, and there's one thing about these mountain boys," he continued, "they were always making time for crimes on what we call an 'installment plan.' In other words, if they had ten years, or whatever they had, they would always figure on escaping two or three times and not making it solid. That's what they called the installment plan."

Caledonia, Chains and Poison Ivy

In late 1922 Marsh was again moved, this time to Caledonia Prison Farm, on the banks of the Roanoke River.

"I remember that there was a big long dike that had been built with prison labor, using wheelbarrows and shovels and plain hard manual labor. I did not help build this. It was there before my time," Carbine recalled.

"Ross, I got into some trouble at Caledonia, and that's for damn sure. If a certain fellow had showed up at a place I designated one night, there would have been serious trouble," he vowed. "I guess it's fortunate he didn't show up. That night I was, as usual, armed with one of the daggers I had made in prison.

"Caledonia Prison Farm was a bad place for white men. To be factual about it Caledonia was pure hell. I wore a lot of chains in my days. Chains by themselves are bad enough but at Caledonia there was lots of poison ivy, and I always did catch the stuff easily. Some folks are not bothered by it but I sure was," Carbine emphasized. "I had it so bad several times that I ran a fever with it. I had on my chains, and to assist you in getting about you had to wear a leather strap just above the calf of your leg. You hitched your chains up in that leather strap to keep them from dragging and tripping you continuously. The chain stretched from one ankle shackle across to one on the other ankle. It was hot and I remember my leg swelled up so that when I walked, the calves of my legs actually jarred. That was misery as few people have ever known it.

"We did all kinds of farm work," he continued. "We planted and raised cotton, wheat and other crops. I remember once we picked cotton that had frost on it. We burned a lot of wood and I was a good saw filer, so I had the job of keeping the saws sharp. Even doing this we worked in that poison ivy. It was a mess all right and tempers often reached the boiling point."

Riot in the Mess Hall

"I remember once a riot started in the mess hall. This was after new barracks had been built. I guess them fellows had good reason to riot," Carbine surmised. "I know they had a real riot, and that's for sure. I remember that it got so bad that they called out the National Guard. It was a mess all right. You could see things flying in every direction. Guards were turning the screen doors wrong side out getting out the best and fastest way they could. Some of the prisoners would grab their uniform caps and throw them out behind the guards as they ran. I remember seeing a coffee pot sailing through the air with coffee flying out of the spout as it passed. Honestly, it was right funny to see," he grinned, "especially since I was on the inside of the action.

"I was always kind of a lone operator. I came and went as I pleased and I never had to worry about being with the boys. One thing was a little difficult: that was trying to enjoy the riot and wanting to laugh without showing it on your face."

Running Out from Under the Guns

"Some happenings were much more serious and not a laughing matter at all," Carbine explained, the tone of his own voice becoming more sober. "Some of the prisoners felt that they could not stand it any longer and they actually tried to 'run out from under the guns.' I have seen men try this right out in the middle of a cotton field. Some of the fellows made it and many did not. The guards did not know what it was to fire a warning shot. They shot to kill.

"At other times men would figure out ways to escape at night," he continued. "Now when men are confined and all of them have the same idea of getting away in their minds, you would be surprised at the plans that they come up with. You must remember that there was always a guard stationed inside. Also, there were two guards, one on each side looking through the windows at you. The bunks were about four feet from the windows. This space between the bunks and the windows was called the 'dead line,' and if you crossed that line, one of the guards would shoot you. Remember now, there were between fifty and seventy-five men in each of these buildings."

Escape Under the Toilet

"One time a group of these prisoners managed to dig a tunnel under the toilet arrangement," Carbine reminisced, obviously beginning an entertaining episode. "On a chosen night the guard was walking around inside the building and a group of prisoners were gathering around the toilet. The guard could not see what was going on. Every few minutes one of these men would lift up a board and one of the prisoners would drop down in the tunnel and start out. That crowd of prisoners kept getting smaller and smaller, and the prisoners remaining behind kept standing closer and closer together and milling around faster and faster to keep the guard from realizing what was going on. That guard finally began to realize that the group was getting smaller and smaller. At least twenty men made it out that night.

"One I remember in particular. This was a big Russian that we all called Joe," Carbine said, indicating with outstretched hands the breadth of the prisoner's shoulders. "He was powerful and exceptionally big. We didn't know if Joe was gonna make it through the hole or not. It was decided that he would wait until last to try—in case he could not get through the hole—to be sure that he didn't get stuck and block the way. Two or three men waited on the outside to see if Joe was gonna need any help. They had decided that, if necessary, they would grab his arms and force him through. Fortunately, he made it.

"I did not see what was going on outside but it got funnier and funnier inside, watching that crowd of men getting smaller and smaller. The toilet was sitting on an elevation of about one foot. Prisoner after prisoner slipped under that board and made the way to freedom. When the escape was realized, there was plenty of action and excitement on Caledonia that night!" Carbine exclaimed.

Letters Home

During his first years of confinement, Marshall Williams became convinced that he had caused enough trouble for his family. He refused to write home and expressed the wish that his family forget about him. Later he admitted that among the principal reasons for his not writing home were that he resented having to write on stationery with a prison heading and he did not like having his mail censored.

His failure to write caused great concern for his family, especially his mother. Desperate to know if her son was well, she wrote a letter to Captain H. T. Peoples, begging his assistance in convincing her son to write home. The following reply was received by Mrs. Williams on May 18, 1923.

Your letter of several days ago received. We have been so busy planting our crops I have hardly had time to answer your letter. Soon after I received your letter I talked to Marshall about writing to you. He told me that he had written the following Tuesday. I am sure you have received the letter before my reply could have gotton to you. Anyway, I want to say to you that Marshall is getting along fine. I have placed him in a good easy job where he can follow his talents, work out his mechanical ideas, and so forth. I shall do everything in my power to help the boy. With kind regards I remain

Yours very respectively,
H. T. Peoples

"They had difficulty in getting me to write letters home, at first," Carbine confirmed. "I just didn't like it — I mean using that letterhead that had a prison address on it. Later there was some serious trouble in the camp and writing to anyone was prohibited. You weren't even allowed to have a pencil. Some of the prisoners smuggled letters out. They were smear letters and they caused plenty of trouble. You were issued pencil and paper only when you were wanting to write home.

"I wrote to my ma and pa, mostly Ma," Carbine continued. "I got in trouble on account of a letter one time. I was 'A' grade and there was a bastard named Schofield who was secretary to Captain Peoples. I had a prisoner mail a letter for me and I asked some of my people to come up and see me some time at night. My folks wrote a letter back and this Schofield got the letter out of the mail and showed it to Captain Peoples. We lined up one morning. Peoples had the letter in his possession and right away I lost my 'A' standing and was made 'C' grade, which included chains."

This reluctancy to write home came to an abrupt end when Marshall Williams began to develop his ideas for weapons. As he began to conceive new ideas, he quickly realized that he must have descriptive material on weapons already in production. Too, he needed to know more about tools, about patent laws. As well, he needed to look at tool catalogues, for he had in his mind the plan to make his own tools from scraps of metal and materials at the prison. Marshall Williams eventually came to the point where he could hardly wait for the next authorized date to mail a letter to his mother.

On May 1, 1976, David M. Williams, Jr. discovered and turned over to me one of the most important finds of my research. He found that his father had carefully filed away in a trunk every letter he had written home to his mother. It became immediately apparent that Marshall Williams' mother was extremely close to her son — that she recognized and understood his complex mind. She wrote almost daily to companies and organizations to request books, catalogues and gun manuals for Marshall. (It remains a mystery as to where or how Marshall Williams found out where to write.) As a prisoner her son could not write directly to anyone other than his family. His not being able to make direct weapons' inquiries was a great handicap to his progress and undoubtedly worked a hardship on his mother. Mrs. Williams, however, never complained.

Marshall Williams, like all prisoners, was allowed to write only one letter every two weeks, and that only one page in length. He utilized these letters to the fullest and it is quite noticable that he reduced drastically — and at points almost completely deleted — any messages to his brothers or to his wife. He needed the space to detail places and people that he wanted his mother to write. At one point he explained that although his family should not expect long letters from him, he wanted to hear from home often, and that the letters should be in detail, providing information on everyone and everything on the farm.

As the days, weeks, months and years passed, the excitement of his accomplishments is apparent as Carbine's inventions began to materialize. One can also feel the pain of frustration as he sought leave to go to Washington to explain to a patent attorney one of his ideas. Apparent also is his struggle to prove that what he was doing was important, and that to accomplish his aims he must receive a parole or pardon.

The following are excerpts from Williams' letters, beginning in 1922 at Cary Prison Farm and ending in 1927 at Caledonia Prison Farm.

Letter to Tiny (Miss Maggie, his wife) dated March 5, 1922:

[Now in prison, Marshall Williams guardedly asks his wife to have his brother-in-law Columbus McLellan examine a rifle. What the prison officials did not know was that the rifle he was concerned about was the "important" rifle—the one he carried on the fatal day at the still.]

"There is one thing I want Columbus to do and that is to be sure, without fail, to get the Krag and look it over and tell me how it looks when he comes. Be sure and don't 'kid' me about it." [This rifle had been buried.]

Letter dated to Tiny, dated March 19, 1922:

[Carbine's mother had expressed concern about her son's maintaining good morals while in prison.]

"Tell Mother not to worry. As you know I never learned to name a deck of cards nor do I ever intend to. Never worry. I'll make out of this the best that I can. Someday this will be over. I may be down and out but that doesn't matter. The race belongs to the strong anyway and I know everything someday will be better than ever."

Letter to Tiny, dated June 17, 1922:

"Never worry about me. Everything is coming on as could be expected. We will leave here soon. I don't know where. Will write when I arrive at the other place."

[Marshall Williams did not know that he was being sent to a special prison camp for hard-boiled prisoners.]

Envelope containing a drawing dated December 5, 1922:

[A bolt-action rifle was drawn on a Voice of Christ Christmas card that evidently had been sent to the prisoners. Writing or drawing paper was almost non-existent.]

Letter to his mother, dated March 2, 1924:

[Williams' thirst for new technical knowledge was unquenchable:]

"Write Victor J. Gunns & Co., Washington, D.C. for patent laws and laws concerning the use of powder gases that is generated by the cartridge as in gas operated rifles and machine guns, and is there laws that prohibit the use of said gas *provided it is used in an entirely different method or system.* Get me patent drawings of the Mondragon gas operated rifle invented by Mexican Army. Also the Lebel gas operated rifle Model 1917 or latest model. Write Colt Pnt. Firearms Co. Hartford for a booklet on their machine rifle and Browning machine gun. *I want action as soon as possible."*

Letter to his mother, dated May 5, 1924:

"I need the paper mentioned [mechanical drawing paper]. Tell Columbus if he can get it bring me a few pieces of broken Packard springs or ' cats ' will do. Let them be taken from the middle to the bottom if he can."

[These items were soon to be made into beautiful and deadly knives. Williams also made some of his early gun parts from these pieces of springs.]

Letter to his mother, May 11, 1924:

"I got your box and letter. Also the manuals from the Ordnance Department. Concerning the drawings—I am of the opinion that O'Brien [a patent attorney] could understand them but for some reason he is pretending that he does not. I am here and couldn't very well go and make it plain to him myself. I sent him sometime ago a sketch of the gas system drawn on a Victor J. Evans and Co. blank by special delivery letter. Write him if he has it to return it and let me start it all over new with new drawings.

[Carbine then requested additional information concerning patents:]

"After an invention has been patented can the inventor take any steps that are necessary to improve and perfect his invention without forfeiting his right in any way? Also can anyone use his idea in any way on any system? Explain this in detail."

Letter to his mother, dated June 29, 1924:

"I got the copies of the drawings from you. I intended to send them with this letter. The $25.00 you mentioned. You may send it to them [the patent attorney] for it will have to go sometime, but remind them that you have sent the other which makes $50.00. I sent you a letter with a long mailing list. I will send you another. You should write me more often —especially while this is in process. Write me more often and in detail while this is in progress. I should like a letter Monday and Friday."

Letter dated to mother, July 5, 1924:

"As you probably know I sent you drawings last Tuesday. Also with instructions. There were 2 drawings and five instruction sheets and one clipping from catalogue. Write O'Brien and ask him if he received all eight sheets — also —it is *D. M.* instead of *D. H.* Williams. I don't hear from you often. You should write me more often, twice a week, while this case is in process of filing. I am giving you another mailing list. [Included: Bureau of Inventive Science, American Industries, Inc., *Popular Mechanics* (Bureau of Information), World Progress Publications Company, Francis Bannerman and Company.] Mail catalogues received separately and insure. Concerning the storm. I regret very much the loss of the trees because of their tradition and comradship. What will you do with the walnut? Above all never destroy it. Get it into such a shape that it may be taken care of. I will need part of it soon I guess."

Letter to his mother dated July 26, 1924:

"As you know, Father was here to see me a few days ago. I sent the things [knives] to you. The large one for Pa and the small one for you. I made the notches back of the blade for you to rest your thumb on while using. You mentioned something about never having been able to get the cartridges from Newton Company but I do not care for them now. I think they have gone out of business. The only ones I want now is .30 1906 U. S. Govt. pointed, full patched bullets. A box of 20. If you are unable to get them in Fayetteville you can get them from Bourne & Bond, Louisville, Ky. but some hardware or pawn shop should have them in Fayetteville. Mother, the knives are not made for heavy bone cutting. I'll make a heavy one for that purpose. Tell Pa and will send it when you all come. I made them for ordinary light meat cutting. An 8 in. saw file to cut them down when they get dubbed off and a whet rock to smooth the edge up is a good way to sharpen them. A *grindstone* will get them out of shape. I don't mean file every time you sharpen them. File them only when they are too dubbed to whet. Wesley and the boys should know. There is an art to sharpening a knife."

Letter to his mother, dated August 3, 1924:

"As I stated before the circumstances under which I draw are [and] have been *discouraging* because I have not very much spare time. Also the place being crowded and inconvenient for drawing. Making additional sketches such as he [the patent attorney] would want, would require a month or more under present circumstances. Perhaps then he would not understand. I am certain that if it were drawn by expert draftsmen they would not get the *full* understanding. I sometimes think they understand but will not admit it. Some other person may file ahead of me and cause me to lose out in law but my own laws would win in the end. I intend to get all that is due me from now on.

"If you could get me a compass (drafting compass) for making circles (0) I would appreciate it. Also a couple pencils (mechanical drafting pencils with small hard leads)."

Letter to his mother, dated August 10, 1924:

"I think I could if I had about $5.00 get a bargain in a drafting set. I am in need of a set if possible. If Leon stays home long and if you go to Dunn, go to the hardware store and get some Winchester gun grease, 1 tube, and have him to clean out my rifles [the Krag and Newton] and pull greased patches through the barrels and grease actions."

Letters from this point on were written on stationery with a prison heading.

Letter to his mother, dated Sunday, February 1925.

[Carbine expressed disappointment over lack of progress concerning a proposed trip to Washington to check on patents.]

"It looks as if we are having bad luck."

[He urged his mother to write C. F. Pease Company, Chicago, for Catalogue No. BC - 24, which lists tracing paper, T-squares, scales, triangles, etc. He then cautioned her:]

"Don't let anyone see the old drawings. They are out of date—if you need to show any let me know and when I make some new ones I'll send them."

Letter to his mother, dated Wednesday, July 21, 1926:

"I noticed a fellow from other camp with 15 years got parole for a few days on a $2,000.00 bond. I am sure if I could get a parole it would lead to something better."

Letter to his mother, dated Sunday, August 8, 1926:

"I am not in a writing mood. I am at present under stress of an unusual type of blues caused by a collision of inventive thoughts on a certain subject on my mind that is hard pressed to solve with other thoughts that come in, in the form of a most lonesome mood. Inventive thoughts in themselves to me are serious, and when other thoughts far more serious and of a most lonesome nature bombard each other at the same time in one small head generall gives me the blues." [Williams' italics.]

Letter to his mother, dated February 13, 1927:

"I would like to call your attention to Col. Albert Cox and Buck Jones. Col. Albert Cox as he is known, if he would, could have more bearing than any other one I know (trying for pardon or parole). The most important point is to get him interested. Buck Jones is a ' wire '—he is also connected to various wires—it seems he has great influence with prison officials. The main idea is to hire them on a ' no action-no pay ' basis. Bear in mind—if they are confident they can do anything they won't mind this plan."

Letter to his mother, dated May 1, 1927:

"It seems like I have great difficulty in hearing from the parties you write for me. As you should know things of the nature referred to are of great importance to me however trivial they may seem to you all. *If I have nothing to*

*passify my mind here it places me in bad circumstances
as I am not sociable.*

"It seems that the great and important things of life
worry me no more than trifles when both are beyond my
reach whereas having accomplished a great thing a person
pays it no concern and on the other hand the trifle worries
him more than the former for reason he hasn't accomplished that."

Letter to his mother, dated Wednesday, May 11,
1927:

"As luck would have it I never became involved in the
recent 'storm' [trouble in prison]. Writing was suspended
Sunday and that is reason for not writing you. [A prisoner
escaped. Marsh noted: 'A friend who can identify himself'
might call on you. The friend was the escaped prisoner.]

"I noted what you said about what the Sheriff said.
This is the point. If the people will help do something, I
have no grudge—but—if they withhold their efforts and
use their influence to keep me in trouble and if they continue
to hold a grudge against me why I will no doubt return
their kind feeling to them. At present I have no grudge
against *no man* or *woman.* One of my faults—I'm too easy
to forgive and forget. You will note I have been paid off for
things I have done that other people didn't like whereas no
one has to pay off for things they done to me. Why I must
be a very inferior thing—none of my ideas are right and
everybody elses are. I am not entitled to a single idea of my
own. *If I get out, by the time I have got set, which means
I'll have to start anew, I'll continue to overlook all—but if
not I'll try to dig up all old stuff and have a big wash day!
The sooner I get out the better twill be for all concerned.*
As it now stands I have forgiven all and forgotten all and
the future alone holds power to arise. The Sheriff, for
instance, never passes thru my mind with respects to a
grudge."

Letter to his mother, dated May 15, 1927:

"P.S.: It is suggested that you all put a letter 'A' in the
left corner of envelope when you write so it will be easier
to get my mail."

[This was suggested by an official. Marsh had finally
made "A" grade, a trusty.]

Letter to his mother, May 29, 1927:
[Williams was in trouble again.]
"Under circumstances I don't think your visit will be
enjoyable as could be expected in a sense. I had rather you
all would not come." [He had lost "A" grade.]

Letter to his mother, dated Wednesday, May 9,
1928:
[Williams was recovering from confinement.]
"I'm in fair shape now. I'll let you know when I am
sick enough to warrant it. Maybe June will 'well me up.' It
would be good to be out for I am losing so much time as I
can't move another peg for I have reached the limit of my
equipment. I haven't the machines to go any further as my
work has advanced to a much higher state requiring more
than I have to advance. You shouldn't worry about me."

Handmade Knives

During my visits with Carbine Williams, several ex-
quisite knives and daggers were displayed (Photo 15). All
were made by him at Caledonia Prison. One is described
by Carbine as follows:

"This knife is very heavy. It has brass hearts and
diamonds on the guard, a shiny steel blade and leather
between the brass sections of the handle."

"That *is* a beautiful knife," I admired. "I notice that it
is inscribed here, 'DMW,' and on the other side of the
handle, '1922.' Did that knife ever come in handy?"

"Well, I carried it a lot," was his noncommital response.

"Once when my pa was visiting me at Cary Farms, I
showed him this beautiful dagger with two brass hearts
and the initials 'JCW' on the blade near the guard. I slipped
it to Pa and he brought it to Godwin," Carbine confided.
"Later, Ma entered this dagger in the Fayetteville County
Fair and it won first prize. This dagger is now a part of the
museum display of my shop in the Department of Archives
and History in Raleigh."

Carbine made several extremely handsome knives
while in prison and noted that it was not uncommon for

Photo 15. David Marshall Williams made many beautiful daggers while confined at Caledonia Prison. During his entire stay in prison only one of his daggers was ever confiscated.

almost every prisoner to have some kind of weapon on his person or near at hand. The guards often conducted shake-downs, but during Williams' entire stay in prison he only once lost one of his knives.

Skill with Wood

Williams made other "weapons," too. On one occasion he presented me with a short mallet made of walnut. It has a striking surface of about two and a half inches in length.

"Ross, you can tell Miss Anne [my wife] that this is an ice crusher but, between you and me, when I made this in prison it was a skull buster," Carbine confided.

It was unusual that this genius with metal was also extremely skilled at making items from wood. In my collection is another example of his skill—a rolling pin turned from walnut at one of the prison farms.

Saturday Baths

"The wash house and the shop were in the same building," Carbine noted. "One end was the shop and the other end was the wash house. The boys would all come here Saturday evening to bathe, and all the ones that had chains on them would have to come into the shop so that I could cut off the chains so that they could take their britches off."

"They were actually bradded on each time?" I inquired.

"Oh yes," he replied, "I've got the hammers I made and used to cut the rivets. They'd come in there and get their chains cut off and put on each Saturday. I had my guns in there but nobody ever said nothing to me about them. I reckon it's just the way that you get along with folks.

"When you had your gun and tools in there and those men were all around, they knew better than to mess with them. That was your business."

Photo 16. This is the first weapon Marshall Williams ever built in prison, Model No. 1. It was not mentioned in the movie bearing his name nor has it ever been photographed before. For years it stood unassembled, in Williams' smokehouse. At the author's insistence, the inventor completely restored this weapon.

At this time, Marshall Williams had completed only one of the three rifles that he had invented. This was the Model No. 1 (Photo 16).

"Yes, it was mine and they knew it!" Carbine said with jaw firmly set. "If I could do them a favor anytime I would, as long as it was in order and not double-crossing anybody. I admit that once in a while, when putting chains back on a man, that they might fit a little looser than usual if he seemed to have itchy feet or be planning to serve his time on the 'installment plan,' " he said, becoming jovial once more.

Tensions Run High

Carbine told of other incidents in prison. To offer an example of the pressure under which these men lived, he told the story of two boys that he called "the Joneses," who were resting on a bunk beside him in the barracks one day. For no apparent reason and saying nothing, these two brothers got up and started beating their mattresses to pieces.

Carbine remarked, "Anybody that had any raisin' wouldn't start beating their mattress all to pieces like that for no apparent reason." The boys took exception to this and went around the end of their bunk and got a club.

"I bounded out of my bunk with a hand ax," Carbine said, scarcely displaying emotion when relating the dramatic event, "and we were gonna fight. I still didn't know what had made those boys take such an exception to what I'd said, until I found out later their mother was running a sporting house in Asheville, North Carolina. Well, I didn't know that, and had I known such a thing I wouldn't have made such a comment. We reconciled this argument and later we became pretty good buddies.

"These are the same boys," he continued, "that later ran slap out from under the guns and they had to go about a mile before they hit the Roanoke River. They were good swimmers, no question about it. But it was a hot day and they must have caught the cramp when they jumped in, for both drowned. They found them at what they call 'Buzzard's Bay.' They brought these boys back in a pick-up truck and left them out under a shed there for awhile and had them put in some kind of a box, and their mother came from Asheville and got them."

Gordon and Leon Williams related another event told them by Carbine that further demonstrated cruelty at Caledonia. If a prisoner attempting to escape was shot, the body was hitched behind a mule and dragged like a log through the field in front of other prisoners to discourage them from attempting to escape. The bodies were laid up under shelters in the open so they could be viewed by other prisoners.

In the Dark Hole

Fate often deals strange hands in the least expected ways. Such was the case when, for a minor incident, Marshall Williams was confined in the "dark hole" or "box" by Captain H. T. Peoples.

Before giving Williams' account of the incident, I must explain that the dark hole was a severe form of punishment given a prisoner who dared to defy the guard's orders or prison rules. The box — with its hard, rough, wooden floor and fitted inside with chains — was intended to discourage any prisoner from considering escape, no matter how desperate he might become. The box was less than head high, for even the shortest man, and not nearly long enough to lie down or stretch out in. Old-Timers will better understand the structure when I say that it was quite similar to a very low version of the old outhouse that used to be so common around farmhouses.

"Yes, Ross, I was confined in the dark hole," Carbine confirmed, "that's for damned sure! I want to make something clear in the beginning: I wasn't put there for doing nothing mean. I guess it was all a big misunderstanding all the way 'round.

"It was in the summertime and hotter than forty hells. We had just returned late that evening from working down in the Caledonia swamps on the Roanoke River. It was no place for man or beast to live or work. We were just starting for supper. A fellow I knew and liked in prison was bad sick with a kind of fever. I remained behind in the barracks with him and was real late getting to supper. Everyone else had gone in. When I walked in, Captain Peoples had plenty to say about my being late and about my violating his rules. Well, in fact, he plumb bawled me out, for sure.

"I started to explain that I had a damned good reason for being late," Carbine emphasized, "that I was helping a sick man. Well, he had some more to say; I don't remember exactly what, but it was more or less threatening me with confinement in the dark hole. Being young and not thinking, I mouthed off at him in front of the other prisoners, telling him that I would go to the hole any time for a sick friend. I guess I put him on the spot, more or less. He showed me who was boss for damn sure. He said, 'Put him in the hole until he expresses an apology to me,' and in the hole I went.

"That's the way things go sometimes," he added. "Even when you think you are right, you are wrong. It was a mistake all 'round."

"Carbine, I understand that you set a new record for both stubbornness and for length of confinement in the dark hole. Is that correct?" I asked.

"I reckon so. That's what they say. I'm told that a man stayed seven days once. I was there for a long month! I know one thing. I lost so much weight that I could feel every bone in my body when I tried to sleep on that rough, hard floor."

"Carbine," I asked, "was there ever a time when you considered offering that apology you were told to give?"

"*NO!*" he said emphatically.

"You lost so much weight, Carbine," I reminded him. "What were you fed?"

"They gave me two cups of water and two slices of bread a day."

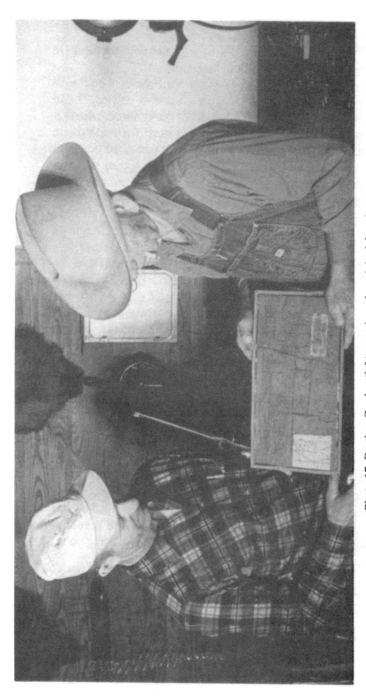

Photo 17. Brother Gordon (left) examines the original drawing made by inventor Carbine Williams while in prison. Gordon, too, had a wealth of knowledge concerning weapons and often assisted his brother.

"How did you have the strength or determination to tough it out?" I asked in amazement.

"I was determined that Captain Peoples would take me out of that hole, and he did," Carbine smiled. "I had read someplace in a dime novel that the Chinese, when experiencing torture or pain, would keep their minds on subjects that required deep thought or concentration, and in this way their mind could not totally record the pain they were enduring. Ross, I have always loved guns, so I began, in my mind, to assemble and disassemble every gun I had ever owned.

"I tell you, I could see in my mind the inside of weapons as though they were in color. I could see the firing pin strike the cap of the cartridge, the explosion of the powder, the movement of the bullet through the barrel, and I began to examine the vast amount of energy that was being wasted, especially in automatic weapons as the bolt was blown back. I began to get the idea of the floating chamber, looking at it somewhat like putting your foot on a croquet ball and then driving another ball by hitting the one you had your foot on with the mallet. Also, I saw the gases burning and realized, some damned how, that this energy should be captured and used. You will never know how many thousands of times I thought and rethought these ideas while hurting in that box.

"I had lost plenty of weight and was in bad shape when they took me out of that hole, but as soon as I was able, I began to get my ideas in order. I began to make myself a ruler and started finding scraps of paper on which I could record my ideas (Photo 17). It was truly a bad time, but overall, a very important time in my life—a turning point, for sure.

"Oh, yes," he added, "one more thing that might interest you. Later on, while I was running the blacksmith shop for Captain Peoples, he came to me and asked that I build him a row of dark holes, or 'the hole' as they were called by the fellows that worked with me. I knew something about them, so I did build eight of them in a row, made out of heavy timber about four inches thick with long bars running along the sides. The ones I built were a little better than the one I was confined in."

Spike Bending

Among the amusing stories related by the Williams family is the story of David Marshall Williams' bending spikes. The source was Carbine's brother Gordon.

"Marsh, as you well know," he began, "had *very* strong hands. He took great pride in his strength. This strength was developed in a most unusual way. While Marsh was confined in prison, he worked in the blacksmith's shop and one of his duties was to serve as a human vice. He used his hands as a vice to hold small metal parts being made with a file. It required tough and very strong hands, for the piece being held could not be allowed to slip. To build this great strength in his hands, Marsh used to bend sixty-penny nails with his bare hands.

"Now, having plenty of time and being determined to be very strong," Gordon continued, "Marsh would not just bend a nail now and then. He would open a hundred-pound keg of nails and start bending until he had bent all one hundred pounds into the shape of hairpins. Next he would reseal the keg of nails and ship them on the next wagon to another prison, wondering what the other prisoners and officials thought when they opened a new keg of nails and found all one hundred pounds bent."

I can attest to Williams' ability to bend nails, for once, while visiting Carbine in his shop in Godwin, we were taping an interview and a discussion began about Williams' being referred to as the "Ol' Spike Bender."

"Let me show how it's done," Carbine offered. With this he picked up a sixty-penny nail, held it out at arm's length, and with his powerful hands bent the nail into hairpin shape. He smiled and threw me a spike, suggesting that I bend one. I not only could not bend it freehanded but I was barely able to put a slight bend in the spike on the edge of the table.

Framed in my gunroom is a photograph of Williams, under which one of these bent spikes is mounted. Written under this is: "REB, this is why they call me the spike bender. You saw me do this right here in the shop. When you get to be 63, you bend one for me. Carbine Williams."

I fear that I will never accomplish this feat at any age, for I certainly don't have, and know few men who do have, such strength in their hands.

Influence of a "Most Unforgettable Character"

In all of my research I have found no better accounting of Carbine's time at Topton and later at Caledonia, under the supervision of Captain H.T. Peoples, than the article which Peoples (Photo 18) wrote in the March 1951 *Reader's Digest* magazine.

Captain Peoples was in charge of Topton, in Graham County, North Carolina, and, when this camp was closed, was transferred to Caledonia, where he was made superintendent of Caledonia State Prison Camp. Marshall Williams was under his command at both locations.

My Most Unforgettable Character — Carbine Williams[1]
by Captain H.T. Peoples

I first saw David Marshall Williams nearly thirty years ago. Shackled by leg irons to four other prisoners, he had just finished an exhausting hike from the railway station to our labor camp in the Blue Ridge Mountains of North Carolina. The other men were limping but not Williams, although one of his shoes was stained with blood from the chafing of the leg iron. He was a sandy-haired broad-shouldered youngster, his light blue eyes hard and unsmiling.

He had been convicted of killing a prohibition officer during a raid on a whiskey still in the hills. [Actually, it took place in the swampland of eastern North Carolina, near Fayetteville.] Twenty years old, he had a thirty-year sentence ahead of him.

---

[1] © *Reader's Digest*, March 1951. Reproduced with permission.

Photo 18. The David Marshall Williamses had a reunion with Mr. and Mrs. H. T. Peoples (right) after Peoples, Williams former prison superintendent at Topton and Caledonia, wrote of his experiences with the inventor in the May 1951 *Reader's Digest.*

'You men know why you're here,' I said, as the group came to a halt. 'They found you hard to get along with up at the state penitentiary. They tell me you're trouble-makers. Well, behave yourselves here and you'll be treated square. Try to escape and you'll get drilled through the head.' A rough speech — but the men we got were rough. And so was the life they led: pick-and-shovel work in leg irons from five a.m. until six p.m., with half an hour for lunch; sleep on wooden planks in a bunkhouse holding fifty prisoners, all shackled to an iron bar running from bunk to bunk.

In the first month I don't believe young Williams spoke more than twenty words to anyone. The other prisoners seemed to realize that he was different from the ordinary criminal. He was. His father was a prosperous farmer with more than two thousand acres of land. His older brothers were either already launched on successful careers or studying in eastern universities. Marshall was the lone black sheep.

In going over the outgoing mail I noticed that Williams never wrote home. Finally, a letter came to me from his mother imploring me to persuade him to write. When I called him in, he said, 'I don't want to write home from a prison postmark. I've hurt them enough already.'

'Mothers don't forget their sons,' I said.

He looked at me steadily with those bright, intense eyes. After a moment he said: 'I was a crazy kid to get mixed up in that moonshine business. I never killed anyone — never. But all of this could kill my mother and father. Somehow, I'm going to make it up to them. I'm going to make them proud of me.'

About a week later Williams requested a pencil and some sheets of paper or cardboard. Believing he had decided to write a letter, I agreed.

But it wasn't a letter. Late one night I walked in the bunkhouse to find Williams, left leg shackled as usual, hunched over on one side of his plank cot. On a piece of cardboard, using a stubby pencil and the straight edge of a shingle, Williams was making a drawing. I noticed the shingle-edge had been nicked to mark sixteenths of an inch. He looked up quickly at my footsteps.

'Better get to sleep,' I advised. 'I couldn't sleep until I
—' he began, then broke off and withdrew again into his
shell. I knew it would be a long time before the boy would
talk his troubles out with anyone. But I had noticed that
the hard, bitter eyes were softening. Whatever he was
doing, it was making him a little happier. Night after night
I passed the bunkhouse door and saw Williams at work
while the other prisoners snored, but I never asked any
questions.

When autumn came our labor camp was transferred
to Caledonia Prison and Williams was put to work in the
blacksmith shop repairing broken-down equipment. I soon
saw that he could do miracles with his hands and decided
to put him in charge. That winter the boy spent even his
nonworking hours in the blacksmith shop.

Going in one evening, I found he had made himself a
drawing board out of packing cases and from some
mysterious source had obtained a set of draftsman's
instruments. [Shell Williams, brother of Carbine, confirmed that the family had sent this set of drawing
instruments, made of German silver, to Carbine at his
request.] I looked at the complicated design on the drawing
board, then at him. He didn't need any urging that night.
As he talked, his eyes literally shone.

'It's a detail drawing for a new kind of gun,' he explained. 'Don't worry,' he added, smiling. 'This has nothing
to do with an escape. I wouldn't try to escape now if the
gate was wide open. I've got too much work to do, and this
is a good place to do it. You see, I've been tinkering with
guns ever since I was a kid . . .'

He explained that the present gas-operated automatic
gun took its driving power from the muzzle. The gas drove
a long piston which operated the breech mechanism. It was
necessary to use ammunition with a high muzzle pressure;
there were many other disadvantages.

'So I had this idea,' Williams said, pointing to the
sketch. 'This piston will be only five-eighths of an inch long;
instead of a three-and-a-half inch movement, it will travel
less than a tenth of an inch.'

He brought out another design. 'This,' he said, 'is an
improvement for the recoil-operated automatic gun. At

present, the whole barrel of such a gun moves backward about three and a half inches. One day I asked myself: Why not make a gun in which only part of the barrel kicks back to work the breech mechanism? And that's what this is. Only a small sleeve, the part chambering the powder case of the cartridge moves — less than one-tenth of an inch. Yet this short punch will open the breech mechanism against the resistance of the closing springs. You know how you can hit one croquet ball a long distance by holding your foot on another ball and transmitting the shock of the mallet? It's the same idea.'

I didn't know it then, of course, but what this young prisoner was telling me that night would one day be considered by firearms experts one of the greatest revolutionary advances in gun design since Browning's development of the machine gun. In World War II the short stroke principle was to be embodied in the famed U.S. Army carbine, which increased the firepower of our infantry by at least one third. About eight million of these carbines would be manufactured for our troops in Europe, the Pacific, and, later, Korea. And the 'movable chamber' was to make possible the use of .22 caliber ammunition in training our troops in the use of machine guns. Army Ordnance would one day estimate that this invention had saved the Government millions of dollars.

But that night I only half-listened and protested: 'But all this is on paper. How do you know it will work?'

'I'm going to prove it,' Williams said quietly.

'But gun-making calls for the finest precision machine tools,' I argued.

'They made good rifles by hand years ago,' Williams answered. 'I can do it too.'

All through that year Marshall Williams worked an eighteen-hour day, pushing the prison blacksmith work far ahead of schedule, then turning to his gun-making. First he made a crude lathe out of scrap iron and wood, powering it with an ancient Ford motor from the prison junk yard. Out of the same scrap heap he salvaged a Ford axle which, drilled out with the handmade lathe, became the barrel for his first experimental rifle. The receiver, the basic part of the gun into which moving parts are assembled, was

Photo 19. The author (left) holds the first weapon Williams invented while in prison. The inventor holds the one for which he is most famous, the M-1 carbine.

fashioned from a broken tractor axle. In order to achieve this miracle he was obliged to reduce a piece of steel which weighed more than five pounds to less than twelve ounces. Since he had no milling machine for precision work, every ounce of surplus steel had to be hand filed. I have never seen calluses so thick as the ones on young Williams's hands after that winter of incessant filing.

The more than twenty-five small parts, such as the hammer and trigger, were laboriously shaped with hacksaw and hand-file.

In 1929, after he had served eight years of his sentence, Williams's case was reviewed. He received a full pardon. By that time he had made six guns featuring the short-stroke and movable-chamber principles. Now he went to Washington, obtained patents, and demonstrated his guns before Army experts.

The outbreak of World War II found Williams working as gun designer and inventor for the Winchester Repeating Arms Company. With the Winchester staff of gun designers, he produced the pilot model of the carbine in just thirteen days. Royalties soon began coming in on the carbine and Williams was on his way to fame — and considerable wealth. He had made good on that pledge to me of some twenty years before. Both his father and his mother, fortunately, lived to see him do it.

An extremely reticent man, who rarely talks about himself, Williams last winter was invited to speak before the prisoners at the Carolina State Prison in Raleigh. 'Don't think that because you've been to prison you're finished for life,' he told them. 'It's what you do after you get out that counts. Work hard and keep your nose clean and you'll find that the people who really count will respect you.'

Today, at fifty, Williams does most of his work on the family farm near Godwin, North Carolina. With fifty-two patents to his credit, his name is known and respected by armament experts throughout the world.

A few months ago he came to me with a problem.

'You've always been good about handling things, Cap,' he said. 'Maybe you could advise me about what I should say to my son, David.'

'About what?' I asked.

'About my being in prison. David is twelve now, and somehow I can't bring myself to tell him that his father is an ex-convict who served eight years for manslaughter. I've started a dozen times to tell him, but I just can't come out with it. If he looked at me the wrong way I'd want to walk right out of this world.'

And then this man whom the most brutal chain gang couldn't crack took out his handkerchief and blew his nose hard.

'Why not let me tell him about it,' I asked, 'in my own way.'

His face brightened. 'Would you?' he said. 'That would be great.'

So that is how I came to tell this story, the story of the gamest man I ever knew, of the man who refused to believe that just because you've been to prison you're finished for life.

That was your father, David. This story is for you. Be proud of him.

There is an episode to this story that is not included in the article by Captain Peoples.

According to Carbine Williams, when prison officials in Raleigh found that a "murderer" was "manufacturing guns" in prison, they went berserk. Newspaper articles were published. The Board of Commissioners issued a complaint and Captain Peoples was called in before the superintendent of prisons. The stalwart police officer stood before him and promised: "If Marshall Williams tries to escape with this weapon that he's building, I will serve the balance of his time. I will assume full responsibility. I trust this man."

With Captain Peoples' backing, Marshall Williams continued to design new weapons. Before long Mrs. Claud Williams received a letter containing a set of detailed technical drawings of one of his inventions. They were sent to her in order that patents could be applied for.

"Ma was so excited and proud and just filled with joy knowing that finally things were looking brighter for her son," Gordon recalled. "She was so excited that she could not be satisfied to wait until we got home from school to show us the drawings. Knowing that we had to come by the stable after school to water and feed the mules, and knowing she would be there milking the cow, she carried these drawings with her, excitedly watching for us to come home so that she could share this good news."

CHAPTER 7
Pardon and Return to Godwin

Accomplishments Lead to Pardon

It has been wisely said that time heals all wounds. As such, events began to favor Marshall Williams. First, prison officials who previously had been skeptical about Williams' building guns in prison now became proud of his accomplishments. When the press began to publicize his developments, a number of perceptive politicians quickly joined the ranks of those singing praises of his accomplishments and of the work the prison was doing in rehabilitating him. Through correspondence and through newspaper articles, several gun companies had heard about the inventor and expressed interest in seeing his weapons.

The Williams family, as always, supported Marsh Williams totally, and again and again sought help in getting a review of his case for consideration of a pardon or parole. Contacts to Congressmen, the governor and other important people were made.

The press and some prison officials considered the possibility of a parole slim at best; however, a number of influential people, and public officials who not only enforced the law but saw the value of rehabilitating a man, began quietly to make their views known. Persons like Sheriff McGeachy, who carried Marshall to prison and who initially placed him under arrest, contacted prison officials and governmental leaders in Marshall Williams' behalf.

Captain H.T. Peoples also wrote and spoke out for Marshall's release, stressing the importance of his inventions to America.

Soon unexpected things began to happen. A letter was sent to Mrs. Al Pate, wife of the murdered deputy sheriff, asking her opinion and feelings concerning Marshall Williams' being granted a pardon. Mrs. Pate, after giving the inquiry serious thought, responded, "If he can contribute some good to our country, I will sign for his release." She did just that.

A little later, Marshall Williams was taken to meet powerful J. Edgar Hoover, director of the Federal Bureau of Investigation. The officer in charge began to recite to Hoover the events of Williams' past. Hoover interrupted, saying: "Damn what he was — what is he now?" Like Mrs. Pate, Hoover was willing to offer Williams a chance.

Finally, on September 29, 1929, after many weeks of deliberation and countless letters and forms, Marshall Williams, prisoner 17758, was granted a full pardon by Governor Angus W. McLean of North Carolina. Williams, having served eight years, having performed hard manual labor, having suffered confinement in the dark hole, having built his own tools and having invented and perfected revolutionary weapons, was free to return to his farm near Godwin.

Unlike the days prior to his confinement, Marshall Williams was now mature, a hard man with determination and purpose. Still, he could not foresee the future. He could not know that he would become an internationally known weapons inventor; that his prison experiences would be told by his former prison superintendent in *Reader's Digest*; and that his story would be made into a movie, with Jimmy Stewart playing the role of Carbine Williams. All Marsh Williams had on his mind was to return home, to work in his little homemade shop with his hand-built tools and to bring to reality his ideas for better weapons.

Photo 20. An exciting moment—the author is being instructed by inventor David M. "Carbine" Williams prior to firing Model No. 1, one of three rifles he invented and made in prison.

Photo 21. Men of few words but deep thought, it was not unusual at all for one of the Williams brothers to throw out a thought or comment for discussion and for all three to stand for minutes contemplating a fitting answer or suggestion. Nothing was done in haste. Heated discussions often followed such contemplation. From left to right are Gordon, Marshall and "Shell."

Changes in the Homeplace

Gordon, eight years older when his brother returned from prison than when he departed for prison, recalled vividly Carbine's return home:

"Marsh's return from prison is another moment branded in my mind. I was at the prison gate at Caledonia that memorable day when Marshall was granted his full pardon. Ross, as he walked toward me, he held in his hands that beautiful little .22 rifle which he called Model No. 1 (Photo 20). Captain Peoples had several boxes containing other guns, parts, tools, and so forth, brought out to be put in the car. I stayed as close to Marshall as a shadow . . . . Pa, Shell, Marshall and I got in the car and departed for Godwin."

"On the way," Shell reminded him, "we stuck the .22 barrel out the car window and, while rolling, fired this beautiful little rifle."

Gordon continued his reminiscing: "I was pumping Marsh with questions, and to calm me down he fired out the window; and, as we drove, to keep me a little quieter, he explained every detail of the operation of this rifle to me.

"We arrived at Godwin," Gordon continued, "and stopped at the new home. Marshall had not seen this house, for he had left from the old homeplace, about one-half mile from the new home. Marshall did not feel yet that he was really at home. . . . He was restless and finally he walked from the new house to the old homeplace. Kid-like I followed. I know now that Marshall would probably have rather been alone. We walked down the plantation road, came to the corner of the old grove and approached the place we called the 'gettin' over' place (a point where we always climbed over the fence going to and from school); we passed the buggy shelter, mule stable and the log crib. He stopped at each place and either opened a door or simply touched it. He walked by the old homeplace and did not enter it at that time, past the smokehouse and on to the rail fence that surrounded the old mulberry orchard, and as he crossed this rail fence that was over a hundred years old, I could see that he was breaking emotionally. He stopped, turned toward me and, with tears in his eyes, said, 'Gordon, stay back.' As he walked out in those trees I could hear his prayers and his sobbing. Quite a different man from the one that left through the front gate eight years earlier. . . . He stayed there thirty minutes, occasionally leaning up against a tree, or he would walk a little further and again lean against another tree. Finally, recovering his composure, he returned and together we entered the old homeplace.

"I recall that as we were initially unloading the car, and as we discussed where things were," Gordon said, in his remembrances of Carbine's return home from prison, "Marshall asked about his first store-bought gun, a double-action .45 revolver, a Colt. Ma told him that it was partially disassembled and in a trunk in the old home by the fireplace. He went there, rummaged through that trunk and found the pistol to be missing. . . . Looking *very* stern, he turned to me and said, 'Gordon, do you have my revolver?' I did not. This revolver was never recovered.

"Following these stops, Marshall felt more like he was home. He never referred to the newer home as 'home' but simply referred to it as the new house. 'Home' was the original homeplace from which he departed for prison. Later on, he moved into the old homeplace, restored the house and lived there for a number of years. . . ."

Colt's Initial Contact with Williams

Information has a strange habit of finding its way to the proper source. In June of 1967, I visited Colts Industries, Colts Firearms Division, in Hartford, Connecticut. There I met and was closely associated with a man who became a very close friend, Engineering Project Manager Robert E. Roy. Some months later, Bob Roy wrote me a letter, attaching some items that I consider to be among the most important basic research sources that I have accumulated on Carbine Williams.

The material included a letter dated April 28, 1928, postmarked Columbia, South Carolina, from a W. M. Perry. In the simple penciled note he said: "Enclosed please find a clipping that will probably interest you — W. M. Perry." It is stamped "received" at Colt on May 1, 1928, at 11 a.m.

Perry had attached to his note an article from the *Charlotte News* dated Saturday, April 28, 1928. The headline reads, "STATE CONVICT INVENTS NEW STYLE MACHINE GUN." The article gives details on a weapon invented by Marshall Williams, who was at that time still serving a term in the North Carolina State Prison system.

With this clipping, Bob Roy enclosed a letter to W. M. Perry from Colt Patent Firearms, dated May 1, 1928:

> We acknowledge receipt of your letter of April 28, 1928, with which you enclosed a clipping from the *Charlotte News* relating to an automatic rifle developed by a convict at the State Prison of Raleigh. The information contained in the newspaper article is very interesting and we wish to thank you for having forwarded it to us.

Also on May 1, 1928, the Patent Department of Colt sent a letter to George Ross Pou, superintendent of prisons, Raleigh, North Carolina. Roy also included this letter:

> Our attention has been recently called to a newspaper account of a firearm which has been developed by Marshall Williams, a convict in the State Prison at Raleigh. According to the newspaper account, the Williams invention is applied to an automatic rifle and the rifle is reported to be in some respects superior to such rifles now used by the United States Army. Being manufacturers of automatic rifles we are interested in keeping ourselves informed in all improvements in this line and it would be our policy to cooperate with the inventor who has developed something of genuine merit. We, therefore, make the suggestion to

you that we be informed when Williams is in a position to submit his invention to a manufacturer for consideration.

Finally, in this collection of important papers, Bob Roy enclosed a letter from Superintendent George Ross Pou of the North Carolina Prison system, dated May 10, 1928, and addressed to Colt Patent Firearms Company, Hartford, Connecticut:

> Replying to yours of the first inst. concerning the invention of prisoner Marshall Williams. Beg to advise I am referring this letter to Williams.

These letters comprise the first record of contact between Marshall Williams and the firearms company.

The letter from Colt was referred to Marshall Williams and he had subsequent meetings at the prison with Colt representatives.

Following is the article published in the *Charlotte News* which was forwarded to Colt Patent Firearms Company by W. M. Perry of Columbia, South Carolina:

Charlotte News
Charlotte, North Carolina   April 28, 1928
**STATE CONVICT INVENTS NEW STYLE
MACHINE GUN**
From Raleigh Bureau of the *News* by J. C. Baskerville

Firearm made by man convicted in Cumberland County of murder expected to revolutionize small arms fighting — faster than Browning. An invention that may revolutionize the firearms world, involving radical departures in rapid fire mechanisms as applied to the automatic rifle, has apparently been perfected by Marshall Williams, who for nearly eight years has been serving a term in the State Prison here. For Williams has just completed a working model of this automatic rifle that a number of experienced users of firearms declare is superior in a number of respects to the Browning Automatic Rifle used during the World War.

'It not only is a beautiful appearing gun but the new principles involved in it appear to be perfectly practical,' said Edwin B. Bridges, Commissioner of Pardons, who with George Ross Pou, Superintendent of Prisoners, and several others witnessed the demonstration of the gun within the last few days. 'If the gun is found to be practical—and there seems to be every indication that it is practical—I see no reason why the U.S. Government shouldn't adopt the gun as part of its regular ordnance, for the gun not only fires as rapidly but has longer range than the present automatic rifles used by the United States Army. In addition, it has a nonjamming mechanism and this should be very inportant. There is no doubt that Williams has something entirely new in the firearms world.'

Parole Is Sought

Because of his invention, Williams' friends are seeking a temporary parole so that he may personally attend to the patenting of his invention. Williams was convicted of second degree murder in 1921 in Cumberland County at Fayetteville for killing a deputy sheriff. He was just twenty-one years old at the time. A sentence of from twenty-two years and eleven months to thirty years was imposed by the courts. During the eight years he has been in prison, most of the time at Caledonia Prison Farm, Williams has been an honor prisoner and because of this, Governor McLean recently reduced his sentence to from ten to twenty years. So, if he maintains his good behavior, Williams will complete his sentence in the next two years. However, because there has always been a strict rule against the granting of parole to permit prisoners to attend to personal business matters, there does not seem much likelihood that Williams will be able to get a parole. 'As much as I would personally like to see Williams paroled, especially if it would help him market his invention, under existing rules I do not think there is much chance,' said Mr. Bridges.

'That Williams is a mechanical genius is readily admitted by all those who have come in contact with him,' according to Mr. Pou, Superintendent of Prisons, 'and his ideas have often helped solve difficult problems encountered at various times in construction work about the prison farm. While Williams has always been rather queer and has been regarded as something of a nut by the other prisoners, he has maintained a splendid record from the first and has won the confidence and trust of his superiors,' said Mr. Pou. 'Since he has been at Caledonia most of the time, I have not been able to know him personally as well as if he had been here at Central Prison. However I have known of him for years and have tried to help in every way possible.'

Expert Craftsman

At Caledonia Farm he has been given the free run of the workshop and machine shop there and he has done all the work on his various inventions after his regular duties were completed. That he is a careful, accurate and meticulous craftsman is indicated by the model of his automatic rifle. For though the stock is made of a piece off of an old plow and all the many parts manufactured by himself in the shop at the farm, the gun has the appearance of a machine manufactured article.

Prison officials are doing all they can to aid Williams and are hoping that he will not only be able to patent his rifle but that he will be able to become independent as a result of his invention.

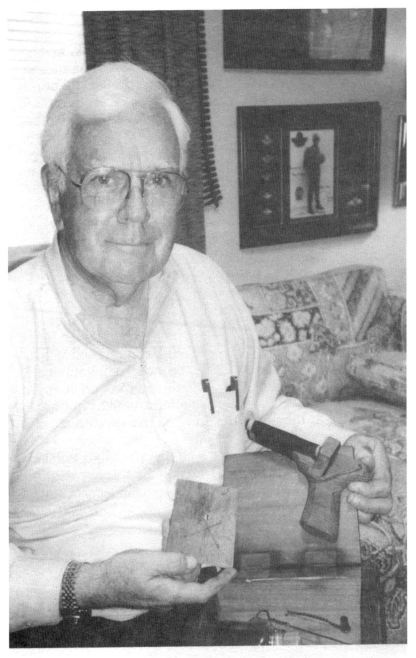

The author holds the wooden pistol.

CHAPTER 8
Williams' Weapons

While several of Carbine Williams' weapons have been photographed repeatedly to illustrate articles concerning his inventions, some are relatively unknown to the shooting world. Some of the little-known weapons have special significance in that they were built by Marshall Williams while he was confined in prison. The inventor's comments in the following subchapters give insight into his inventive ability and his determination to have absolute perfection in his lesser-known weapons as well as in those which have received international acclaim. Each weapon has some characteristic indicative of his inventive genius and each has contributed to the betterment of weaponry in America.

The Wooden Pistol

Certainly one of the earliest, most unusual and most photographed weapons made by Carbine Williams was the wooden pistol that he made as a ten-year-old. I asked Williams to describe this childhood weapon and to provide details concerning its operation.

"I guess I was around ten years old when I made my first wooden pistol. To begin with, it shot black powder, buckshot and paper wadding. [Years later, when demonstrated by Carbine, he used toilet tissue as the wadding.] To make one of these weapons I used a reed, like you fish with, for the barrel. I cut out the partition between the joints and drilled a small hole in the breech end of the reed, which I call the 'touch hole.' The pistol grip I carved from juniper wood using my pocket knife. The reed barrel is first wrapped with strong twine or fishing cord to reinforce the barrel so that it will stand a good charge of black powder. You then wrap the barrel to the pistol grip with the same kind of twine."

Carbine continued: "The ignition takes place by way of an old-fashioned kitchen match with the head snipped off and clamped in place over the touch hole by means of a piece of corset stay that slides in and out under the string wrapping. The hammer is wooden and has a nail head driven into the hammer face. The hammer is operated by thumb release and is powered by rubber bands. When the hammer is thumb released, the nail head strikes the corset stay holder, which crushes and ignites the match head, which in turn flashes through the touch hole, igniting the black powder that has been measured and packed into the barrel. This blows the buckshot and paper wadding out the front of the barrel [hopefully]. There have been several occasions when, due to intentional or unintentional over-loading, the weapon exploded. Ross, she will shoot through a good half inch of wood, easy," he said with pride.

"The really fancy, cased model," he continued, "has a number of important accessories: namely, a .32 empty shell, fitted with a wire handle that is used as a powder measure; another piece of strong wire, sharp on one end and with a loop in the other end that is the touch hole cleaner; then there is a carefully carved ramrod for packing the powder and ball in the barrel. Finally, the case contains three glass bottles. The first contains extra match heads for ignition, and this bottle is wrapped with spare rubber bands. A second bottle contains black powder that I made in my mother's oven, and the final bottle contains either buckshot or small shot."

The wooden pistol weighs less than eight ounces and, when fired, gives no sensation of recoil (Photo 22). The wooden pistol was once demonstrated at Fort Bragg,

Photo 22. Williams displays a wooden pistol, the first weapon he invented at age eleven. Cased with the pistol are a bottle of homemade powder, a bottle of match heads used for ignition, ramrod, touch hole cleaner, unique powder measure, extra rubber bands for the hammer and shot.

Photo 23. "To my knowledge there is no word in the dictionary for this rifle; it recoils forward when fired. It has no breech mechanism so the entire barrel moves about six inches forward. The barrel in moving forward removes itself from the expended cartridge and, as it returns to its original position, picks up a new round and is ready to fire again. I was told it couldn't be done so I did it," Williams grinned.

North Carolina, for the entertainment of General (then Lieutenant Colonel) William Westmoreland and a Captain Mason.

Miss Maggie recalled an experience involving the little wooden pistol: "Marsh had an accident at age ten with this little pistol, shooting his hand," she pointed out. "He carried this scar as long as he lived as a reminder of gun safety."

Carbine Williams noted that years later the U.S. Navy experimented with pressure wire-wrapped rifle barrels. Still later, when the Japanese were running out of steel for guns during World War II, they too tried to wire wrap rifle barrels to save steel.

Williams presented me with one of the two remaining wooden pistols, cased with the accessories, during a 1964 visit to Godwin. The highlight of the presentation occurred when the inventor loaded and fired, inside the shop, the wooden pistol. As always, Carbine Williams' aim was true. I still have the wooden target that was shot that day.

The Rifle with the "Blow-Forward" Action

The "blow-forward" rifle incorporates the most radical weapons design ever produced by Carbine Williams and is one of his vital contributions to weaponry. Yet, it is one of his forgotten inventions. In order that one might acquire some understanding of the operation of this rifle, it will be helpful to refer to Photo 23. To my knowledge, there is no official weapons terminology which explains the operating principle of this rifle. This increases the difficulty of describing it.

First, the weapon has no breech mechanism, as do other weapons. Next, unlike any other weapon, if fired, the entire barrel of this rifle moves forward about six inches simultaneously with the movement of the projectile. As it does so, the barrel removes itself from the expended cartridge, which then ejects. As the barrel returns to its original position, it picks up a new round and the rifle is ready to fire again. I like to say that this rifle "recoils" forward.

In fact, it completely reverses the actions of a conventional automatic rifle. When one fires the weapon, rather than getting the sensation of a recoil, he gets the feeling that the rifle is moving forward. Ever so quickly it compensates for this action by returning to its original position, to a degree neutralizing the "recoil" action.

"Ross," Carbine pointed out in describing the rifle, "it reduces the barrel length by five or six inches. You get the same effect as a long barrel but with a much shorter weapon overall. This, like some of my other Caledonia weapons, is mostly 'Ford.' This trigger guard, here, is part of a Fordson tractor. Most of the other parts are made from the same thing.

"I wasn't no trusty then, Ross," he continued, "and I needed something to make the stock for this rifle. I had a trusty working for me in the blacksmith shop, so I sent him out to the mule corral where we kept lots of mules. He dug me up a walnut fence post and brought it to the shop. I carved the stock from that fence post. I guess I should add that I was making this particular rifle kinda on the sly. It was unknown to anyone in the prison. In fact, the trusty didn't understand what in the world I wanted with an old fence post, and I never have been one to explain too much to people," he grinned.

"How long did it take you to make this rifle, Carbine?" I asked.

"I don't know, Ross." Carbine paused. "It was a number of months. You know, I had plenty of time so I didn't keep too close a record of my work time. It was kind of frustrating for this was a totally different kind of mechanism—different from any I had ever thought of, or even tried to make—and there was no previously known principle of this kind to make comparisons to. I casually described this rifle to a prison guard once, long before it was known to exist. He said, 'Williams, you are nuts. There's no way a rifle could fire or operate like that.' It was kinda fun hearing him say it couldn't be done, knowing in the back of my mind that I had already done it. It brought a little fun to an otherwise hard and serious time in my life, while I was serving that 'long-term contract' with the State of North Carolina.

"You might wonder why they had used walnut for a fence post," Carbine said, as though checking to see if I might have missed that detail. "Well, there was plenty of walnut at Caledonia Prison, down in the swamps all along the Roanoke River. They used walnut there like you use pine in South Carolina—for everything."

"Carbine, I am most impressed with the beautiful way every part fits to perfection," I said as I admiringly stroked the rifle. "Where there is a joint, or point where two parts join, you can't even feel the connecting line with your fingernail. It's like you had the finest of precision tools at your disposal."

"Well, in a way I guess you could say I did have the best of tools, Ross, 'cause I made every damned tool I needed as I went along," he explained, with at least a trace of self-satisfaction in his voice. "Many of the tools here on my shop wall today are the very tools that I made at Caledonia Prison. [To make needed gun parts,] I had to take large pieces of metal, heat it red hot, then drop it on an anvil and maybe get in one lick with my hammer to flatten it before it cooled too much. I repeated this act many hundreds of times to get the desired thinness. Finally, using files that I had made, I dressed the metal down to the desired shape and finish. I hand-tempered every piece. I wasn't satisfied until I had every piece fitting to perfection and until I had each seam fitted until it was almost invisible to the eye or feel.

"Assembly and disassembly of this rifle is unique, too," Carbine pointed out. "You simply lift up this little locking mechanism and the insides can be pushed right out, you see. You dismount this piece, pick this up, and once you take the cartridge head and pull this piece up, the whole thing comes right out this way. It's plumb unique, Ross, and damned well put together."

"Carbine," I asked, trying to pinpoint the period of the rifle's development, "did the idea for this rifle, along with your early carbine, come to you while you were con-fined in the 'dark hole'?"

"Ross, a lot of it came to me there," he confirmed, "but once I was taken out of the box, I had to sort out and begin to put on paper the many ideas that I developed in my mind. As you know, Captain Peoples found me drawing out one of my ideas on the lid of a shoe box late one night as others were sleeping. I had made myself a ruler. Later, when my thoughts and doings were more known to Captain Peoples, he allowed my folks to send me a drawing set, which helped greatly. I wish I knew what became of that set of instru-ments," he said, as though he'd half forgotten these treas-ured former possessions.

.35 Carbine Used in "Carbine Williams"

Contrary to popular belief, the rifle used in the film *Carbine Williams,* although a carbine, was not the .30 caliber M-1 carbine which is now world-famous and which was also invented by Marshall Williams. The weapon in the movie was a .35 caliber forerunner to that used by the military (Photo 24). Williams discussed the weapon with me at length.

"This rifle is the actual rifle that I made on Caledonia," Carbine said, pointing to the rifle on his workshop wall. "It was used, of course, years later by MGM making the movie *Carbine Williams.* Jimmy Stewart, who played my part, used it in the movie. He shot it in some of the scenes or, at least, one of the scenes. The M-1 carbine was devel-oped from it. People don't generally know that this is the original carbine.

"This chamber is made from part of a Model-T crank-shaft," he pointed out. "The throw is part of an old main bearing. I made my own tools. Whatever it took, I made it. I used to keep this gun hid in the walls in Caledonia. In the walls of the shop, the boards went up and down. I had me kind of a dummy-trap place, using two boards. It looked like it was all nailed. And I just stuck the gun in there. For a long time nobody knew I had it."

Photo 24. "This is one of the rifles I made on Caledonia Prison Farm around 1924. It is a caliber .35 and has my 'floating chamber.' From this model, pistols, rifles, shotguns and machine guns were made on this same principle. This was the rifle Jimmy Stewart used in my movie, *Carbine Williams*."

Photo 25. Williams holds the most photographed carbine in the world. This weapon is autographed by a number of distinguished Americans, including General Douglas MacArthur and actor Jimmy Stewart.

"If I remember correctly," I injected for verification, "you told me that the way you got to work on it was when the guards would bring in their weapons for repairs."

"Oh yes, I was the armorer there at prison," Carbine acknowledged. "I took care of all the guards' guns at Caledonia. Finally, after it got to the place when I started making my guns, there was a guard at a sentry box right there at the corner where the shop was. Once in awhile, I would take it out there and show it to the sentry out in the box, and say, 'How do you think I'm coming? How do you think I'm doing?' And I asked him if he'd want to shoot it, and he'd say, 'No, not here.' I'd get ammunition, some of them .30-'06 sizes. Some of the guards would bring 'em right down here to the shop, just like nothing at all. Before I 'got out from the gun' [was made a trusty], a guard used to walk with me over to a place where we could shoot. When I got to be a trusty, I'd go by myself. My favorite shooting ground was an old prison cemetery.

"While we're talking about it," he said, handing me a metal object, "I've got a piece of steel here that I shot four holes in (Photo 26). I shot this on the old cemetery grounds, using one of my rifles; I forget which one. Here's this piece of steel that I brought back. I shot a few there with .30-'06s."

"What is the thickness of this steel?" I asked Carbine, amazed that the cartridge could penetrate it.

"Oh, about a good half inch thick. When the bullets hit, see how it cratered that up? The piece of steel was longer than that. I simply struck it up in the ground and shot it. There was no brace or backstop supporting it."

"Was this the gun you used when you were shooting through the steel?" I asked.

"Yeah, one of them," he replied.

Fortunately, Carbine Williams kept an accurate record of the items from which he made the various parts of this particular weapon. The receiver was made from a Fordson tractor axle; the barrel band from the tractor axle; the barrel from a drive shaft; the cocking cam from a Model-T magnet; the buffer from a tractor axle; the bolt from the

Photo 26. "My favorite place for testing the weapons I built in prison was the old prison cemetery. This is a half-inch-thick piece of steel that I used to stick in up in the ground for a target. You can see that my weapons penetrated it with no effort at all," Carbine pointed out.

rear axle of a Model-T Ford; the movable chamber from a rear axle; the extractor right and the extractor left from magnets; and the operating handle from a drive shaft. shaft.

The guard was made from a tractor rear axle; all small parts in the guard from a magnet; the striker spring plug from an axle; the striker from a magnet; and the sear lever, sear and cocking lever from magnets. (The material of the ejector was unidentified.) The closing spring was made from music wire; the stock carved from a walnut fence post; the cap pistol grip made from an axle. All tools used in the manufacture of this weapon were hand made by Marshall Williams.

.22 Weapons for the Military

"Carbine, it is important that we have on record your development of .22 caliber weapons for the military," I explained as I carefully handed him two of his handmade inventor's model—the .35 caliber rifle used in *Carbine Williams* and the .22 caliber, New Service Ace which converted the .45 caliber automatic to a .22 caliber, but which allowed the same operating "feel" as the .45 caliber.

Carbine, being the perfectionist that he was, carried the .35 caliber rifle to the workbench on the west side of his shop, then, satisfied that he had not placed this weapon in the sunlight coming in the window, walked to the opposite side of the shop and laid the New Service Ace on the other workbench. Returning to the middle of the room, lighting his ever-present Camel cigarette and spreading his feet well apart and firmly planted in anticipation of a long recording session, he said, "O.K., REB, which damned one you wanna talk about first?" I selected the .35 caliber rifle.

"It was 1931 that I went to the Ordnance Department with this very rifle with a movable chamber," Carbine said, pointing to the .35 caliber rifle. "The movable floating chamber gives it the power to operate this heavy mecha-

Photo 27. Carbine Williams displays the Colt Service Ace. This pistol, using his floating chamber, develops the same operating energy from a .22 cartridge as is obtained from a .45 automatic. In his other hand he holds the first hand-built .22 rifle utilizing the floating chamber. This was the grandfather of the now-famous Remington Model 550, rated by the experts as one of the world's best rifles.

nism. This is not what you call a .22 caliber mechanism. It's a heavy mechanism and, without the movable floating chamber, it wouldn't operate. [It was from this mechanism that Williams subsequently designed the conversion of the .45 automatic to a .22 and the conversion of the .30 caliber machine gun to a .22.]

"Well, let's talk about the gun itself," he suggested. "This is a receiver and it's made out of the rear axle of a Fordson tractor. The bolt here was made out of some kind of a drive shaft out of a tractor, and also the barrel. The automatic trigger mechanism is made out of the Model-T magnets that were on the flywheel. It was hammered out on an anvil and then filed into shape and then hardened. The whole thing is mostly Ford."

"You built this gun here in the Godwin shop, did you not?" I asked.

"Yes," he confirmed. "This gun I carried to the Ordnance Department where, of course, they saw the movable chamber. I also took a pistol. This is one of the Colt Service Ace pistols, which also has a movable chamber (Photo 27). The movable chamber operates the heavy mechanism with the .22 cartridge in the pistol the same as it does in the rifle."

"Well, that must have resulted in an enormous savings to the government in training and firing it and in the cost of handling," I interjected.

"It sure did!" Carbine said emphatically. "I didn't know the Ordnance Department was interested in a .22 machine gun or even a pistol for training. When I met with them the first time was the first I knew about it. At that time I met with Major Wilhelm and Mr. J. C. Grady, who were heads of the technical staff in the Ordnance Department. I went to see them first. If you had anything of interest, then they referred you to others. If it was artillery, small arms or anything like that, then they steered you where you belonged.

"At that particular time, Major Julian S. Hatcher (he's a general now) was head of the Small Arms Division, Ordnance Department. They saw the guns that I had here which demonstrated, without a doubt, that I could get a great deal of operating energy out of a small cartridge. Major Hatcher, Mr. Grady and Major Wilhelm saw right away that my floating chamber might be the solution to the .22 machine gun that the Army wanted for all the using services.

"I went over to see Major Hatcher (he really knows guns) and he knew, without a doubt, that I would come up with it," he continued. "He knew that these mechanisms require a lot of energy to operate and he was wondering if I could make a heavy machine gun that would pull a belt. I told him I thought so. 'Well,' he said, 'Are you willing to try it?' I said, 'Sure, I'm willing to try it. I'll be glad for something like that.' He said, 'Well, why don't we?' We agreed on a price for one model .22 machine gun. I left there that day with a contract to make one.

"I come back here to this same shop and made one gun in pretty short order," Carbine said, with obvious satisfaction. "It didn't take me but about five or six weeks, roughly, and I went back with the gun. We didn't go out to the regular testing range they had in Washington at Congress Heights. There was a place right there near the Ordnance Department, some medical center. They had a basement and we went there. We didn't walk very far. We went to that basement and my gun worked good. They said, 'We want five more.' I said, 'All right,' and I come back and made five more.

"I made some improvements on the general mechanism but, of course, didn't change the principle," he stressed. "The principle had to remain the same. This is still the only known way of getting a great deal of operating energy out of a small cartridge. In a book I have it's listed as a 'new principle in firearms.' "

"Actually you pioneered a new firing concept. Yours was a new method," I offered, seeking his confirmation.

"Yes. It was a new method, a new principle by which a gun is made. Anyway, I came back here and I don't know how long it took me to make five but, you know, that's quite a job for one man, and it was some months. Those five guns operated perfectly, and Springfield Armory wanted one and the Ordnance wanted one and the Army, too. It took five to go around

"The original model, they just probably kept that," he continued, "because I made some changes that made it better. I've forgotten what I changed—the feed mechanism, the way the barrel fitted or something. Then the gun was sent to the using services and it made such a nice showing it was unanimously adopted by the using services and made at Springfield Armory. I went to Springfield Armory to see that the blueprints were made all right and they were. While we are talking about it, I do have a set of manufacturing blueprints I brought back from Springfield Armory.

"The kinda funny part to me was being such a young boy," he chuckled. "You know, if somebody said something like, 'You're kinda young for you to have all these fellers making something like that, ain't you?' I'd reply, 'I don't know about that.' There were a great deal of draftsmen and so forth at Springfield Armory and they were all busy making measurements and making drawings— and they didn't change a thing. The orders from the War Department were: when making this gun don't change anything; make it as is. No changes were ever made in the gun," he said, making no effort to conceal the pride he had in this particular weapon.

"We also made what they call a training unit, a training unit for converting a Browning into a .22," Carbine added. "But I don't consider that too good because it was a makeshift proposition all the way through. But the Army did use them and gave me a royalty on that, too. Then, of course, Colt made the Service Ace on the same principle and the Colt conversion unit. They are making them right now. It looks like everything I've ever made is still in production."

"And they are still in use all over the world," I added.

"The patents expired in seventeen years and they were in production way beyond the seventeen years."

"Well, the thing that *I* think is so enlightening," I remarked, "is the fact that you walked in not knowing that the government was even looking for guns. You saved them probably eighty percent on every man that was trained and also saved them five years of production and experimental time."

"Well, the chances are they wouldn't have hit on it then," Williams admitted. "You just can't get a lot of men together and expect to do something. If somebody thinks of something new, that's it. When it comes to you, you don't even work for it. It just comes to you. I never had an idea come to me by hard work. It just comes to me. I could be out having a good time, just enjoying myself or something. I never did just sit down and worry about it and say, 'Well, I've got to think of something.' You don't do that. It just comes to you," he reiterated.

"Carbine, would you mind discussing contracts with the government? How do you deal with them?" I inquired.

"Well, you get paid on what we call a royalty basis, so much per gun or so much of the selling price or the wholesale price. You agree on a certain percentage," Williams explained.

"With your new principle of firing, you didn't have much argument with them, did you?" I asked, knowing the response.

"No, I never did have much trouble about that," he affirmed. "Talking about the .22 machine gun again now, about the last trip to Washington on the machine guns, we met in the Munitions Building. It weren't the Pentagon, because it was before they built that. And at that particular time, all the adjutants general of all the United States were there for some meeting. It was in the big conference room where they met, and they had a great big conference table there. I got up on the table with a machine gun, explaining to all the adjutants general about it and also the pistol—the Service Ace pistol that I had made," he said with the far away look so often visible when he remembered happy times.

"I have at one time met all the adjutants general. Let's see, what was the man's name from North Carolina?" he pondered, then finally recalled the name. "General Van B. Metts. I never will forget it as long as I live. General Metts, kidding all the other adjutants general, talked about how some of them were worried about how many North Carolina boys didn't make West Point. He was sure gonna get back at them! He said, 'Look at that North Carolina boy up there. Where are your boys now?' He broke it off in 'em! Of course, I didn't laugh. I didn't pay it no attention. But, of course, I heard that, all right," he said with his chin firmly set. "They just went on with their meeting and didn't say nothing."

Gordon Williams was quite pointed in his denouncement of the advantage taken of his brother Marshall by the government in establishing the unit price paid to the inventor for the initial machine guns that were to be delivered. He was very open in his presentation of heretofore undisclosed facts involved in the acceptance of this low bid.

"Ross, the government really got their money's worth out of Marsh on the development of the .22 machine gun," Gordon revealed. "You see, the government had been working on trying to get a sub-caliber machine gun since 1917 and not one single person had put their foot in the door. Marsh walked in with both the .22 machine gun and the conversion of the .45 caliber automatic to .22 caliber. Typical of the government, they were required by law to open this project for bids. Not one person bid for no one other than Marsh Williams knew how to obtain great operating energy from a small cartridge.

"You must remember another thing too, Ross," Gordon reminded, "Marsh nor the family had any money whatsoever. To be factual, Marsh had only two pairs of bib overalls, two sets of BVDs and one suit. Without dollars he could not buy needed tools, pay for trips or even pay for patents on his ideas. He felt that if he could get this first government contract, it would provide a few needed dollars on which to operate and try to build his future in the gun

NORTH CAROLINA
CUMBERLAND COUNTY

IN THE MATTER OF DAVID MARSHALL)
WILLIAMS' RESTORATION OF CITIZENSHIP)   D E C R E E

This cause coming on to be heard before the undersigned
Judge of the Superior Court at the June Term of Criminal Court
and it appearing to the Court and being found as a fact that
David Marshall Williams filed in the Superior Court a petition
for the restoration for citizenship; that notice of same was duly
published at the Court House door for ninety days prior to this
hearing as provided by statute; and that the said David Marshall
Williams has appeared before this Court and testified as to his
honesty and good behavior since he was pardoned by Governor
A. W. McLean on the 29th day of September, 1929; and that five
respectable citizens to-wit: E. T Markham, T. G. Braxton,
M. G. Starling, R. E. Tomlinson, Sheriff N. H. McGeachy, who
have known the said David Marshall Williams since he returned
from prison have likewise presented themselves and testified
to the Court that the said David Marshall Williams has been
honest, industrious and of good character since his release.

NOW THEREFORE, it is on motion considered, adjudged and
decreed that the petitioner, David Marshall Williams, be and he
is hereby restored to all and the full rights of citizenship
as by law in such case made and provided.

This the 6th day of June, 1935.

(Signed) Henry R. Grady
                                   Judge of Superior Court.

I hereby certify that
this is a true copy of
the original.
    6   1935

C. W. Broadfoot
     Clerk Superior Court

inventing field. As discussed earlier, Marsh was paid $500 each for five units, a price established by the government. The contract also called for the contractor to provide two one-hundred-round .22 caliber cartridge belts for each weapon.

"Man, there was no such thing in the world," Gordon continued, "and Ma and I had to hand sew each of these belts, plus we had to sew several that Marsh needed for testing his weapons. Talk about blistered and torn fingers! Ma made me sit there and sew those belts with needle and thread until my fingers bled."

The bids were opened on March 5, 1932, and Marsh's bid was accepted on March 17 of the same year. Later on, when Major (later general) Julian S. Hatcher found out that the government had taken such advantage of Marsh, he wrote letters complaining bitterly about this, noting that this man's invention had saved the government millions of dollars in training costs the first year.

Upon parole from prison, Marshall Williams had returned to Godwin and restricted himself to the proximity of his family's farm, working night and day on his inventions. As they progressed, and as he developed new ideas and principles, he often received fully automatic weapons from both government and private agencies. He shipped these weapons as well. Yet, he was not legally a citizen of the United States at the time because when he was convicted and sentenced he was stripped of his citizenship. It was not until June 6, 1935, that his citizenship was reinstated (Photo 28).

.22 Service Model Ace

Rumor had it in the summer of 1938 that Colt Patent Firearms Company was soon going to make a sensational announcement, but no one seemed to know exactly what this well-known company would reveal. On July 4 of that year, not one but two new items were introduced: 1) the Woodsmen Match Target Pistol and 2) the new and exciting Colt .22 Service Model Ace, the latter invented by Williams. Marshall Williams' floating chamber had found yet another use.

Made available to the shooting world that summer was an "autoloader" that simulated the .45 automatic's recoil but utilized the much less expensive .22 caliber long rifle, high-speed cartridge. For the shooter who fired the .45 automatic in competition, and for the layman who simply enjoyed shooting the automatic he brought home from military service or purchased from Army surplus, this new weapon was welcomed. For the first time in shooting history someone had found a way to obtain intense operating energy from a small cartridge in a handgun.

Williams had first conceived this idea while in the solitary confinement of the hole, and he had built three rifles during his imprisonment that utilized this system. Later, he had built for the military a sub-caliber training machine gun that not only allowed a savings in ammunition cost but utilized, with minor adaption, existing guns. And now he had presented to shooting hobbyists a handgun that was inexpensive to buy, inexpensive to shoot, and one which combined accuracy with the feel of shooting a .45 caliber weapon.

Colt had offered the Colt's Ace a year earlier, but this .22 caliber weapon was not the same weight and balance as the .45. It did not operate in any way like the Service .45 automatic and, more important, when the .22 Colt Ace was fired, it gave only the sensation of a .22's firing. It in no way felt or responded like the heavier-caliber weapon. Colt's adoption of Williams' floating chamber put the old Ace out of production and set Colt up as the leader in the .22 automatic pistol field.

The shooting public also had a choice as to what to buy. If a shooter owned no pistol at all, he could buy the complete Service Ace for only $60. If he already owned a .45 automatic, he only had to buy "half a gun." Colt offered a conversion kit, consisting of a slide recoil spring, .22 caliber barrel fitted with Williams' floating chamber, slide pin, recoil spring and .22 caliber magazine, for a total cost of $34. No tools were required to convert the regular .45

to the new .22 caliber action. One simply stripped his .45 down, in the manner required for cleaning, and replaced the regular slide and barrel with the kit in minutes. It was generally felt that the conversion kit was preferred to buying the entire Service Ace, for when the .45 match pistol was converted, the same trigger pull was utilized, regardless of the caliber of ammunition used.

It was predicted by experts, and proved true, that Marshall Williams' latest invention would find its way into weapons history. This important invention continues to be an important item offered by Colt. In addition, no one has come up with an invention to replace Williams' floating chamber.

Gordon Williams, commenting on the development of the Service Ace, brought to light an astounding event which occurred during the time that his brother was doing groundwork on this weapon.

"It was a known fact that Marsh had a tendency to overpower his initial models," Gordon revealed. "One night while sleeping Marsh dreamed that a crack had developed in the slide of the model he was working on (an old .45 Colt automatic). As soon as he waked up the next morning he hit the floor, went to this shop, grabbed his big magnifying glass and, on examination, found a crack in the slide almost exactly where he had seen it in his dream."

In 1932 Marshall Williams had demonstrated the floating chamber principle to the military and it was favorably received, along with his .22 machine gun. But attentions were concentrated on the machine gun, which was recognized to be not only the more important training device but also the more significant money saver.

"In developing the .22 machine gun," Gordon explained, "Carbine again overpowered his initial model. During a demonstration in Washington before the weapons genius General Julian S. Hatcher, Marsh became very upset when his model operated so violently that the .22 cartridges going through that converted .30 caliber machine gun completely tore up the receiver, kicking the rear trigger assembly plumb out of the gun. Marsh started making apologies to General Hatcher. But General Hatcher said, 'Don't apologize! We are overjoyed to see that you can develop such operating energy from so small a cartridge. Let it tear out the receiver. We have more for you to convert.' "

Not until Colt bought Marshall Williams' floating chamber idea and put on the market a weapon utilizing this principle did the military service start utilizing this auto loader in its training program.

Remington Model 550 .22 Rifle

Marshall Williams' youngest brother Gordon is slightly smaller in stature than Marsh. But his manner and powerful hands greatly resemble his brother's. Gordon, a man quietly knowledgable in many fields, is well informed on the technical aspects of firearms—especially those invented by his brother. Gordon worked alongside his brother in the development of the Remington Model 550 .22 rifle and recalled many incidents which occurred while the rifle was being completed.

"At one time Marshall was called on by Remington to convert a Remington .22 automatic bottom ejector so that it would fire and operate using the weaker .22 gallery shorts," Gordon recalled. "It was this conversion that utilized the first movable chamber made for .22 shorts. He had developed this chamber earlier, but for use with .22 long rifles. He found through experiments that this conversion would also fire the .22 long rifles .... He bored the barrel out and made a little movable chamber that was held in place when the barrel was screwed back in.

"While developing this rifle for Remington, the arms company shipped twenty thousand rounds of gallery .22s to us at Godwin to test this rifle. We went to the old juniper swamp to be away from fields and houses on the plantation to begin test firing. Marshall loaded tube after tube and poured them in through the stock, and I fired. After considerable time we had fired all twenty thousand rounds with no malfunctions. Had we not been so pressed for time,

I could have utilized those rounds to become one of the world's top shooters," he joked.

"It was during the development work for Remington on the gallery gun," Gordon continued, "that Marsh came up with the idea of developing an automatic rifle (later called the Remington Model 550) that would fire shorts, longs and long rifle .22 ammunition interchangeably. There was no such weapon in existence at that time.

"Marshall sent me to Fayetteville with instructions to buy a cheap .22 bolt-action rifle. Marshall simply would not go to town if there was any way around it," Gordon revealed. "He was constantly pressing on with his projects in his shop, often throwing down a quilt and sleeping a few hours before starting again, after already having worked well past midnight. I went to Montgomery Ward's and explained what I wanted. The salesman told me that he had a rifle in the shop that had a part missing and would sell me this very cheaply. I bought this Montgomery Ward .22 rifle for $5.

"On return from Fayetteville with the $5 rifle," Gordon added, "Marshall instructed me quite emphatically: 'This project won't and can't take long—just a few days.' My job was to draw to minute accuracy the parts as Marsh described them from his mind's picture. The drawings had to be done with a razor sharp pencil so that Marsh could take measurements and make the parts from the drawings. When I had a few spare minutes I would cut out these drawings, assembly them and make them operate.

"Taking a calendar off the wall, Marsh said, 'We will mark off each day to see how quickly we can complete this job.' We worked day and night. This calendar was carefully marked each day. This rifle was completed on the thirtieth workday, which happened to be George Washington's birthday. Marsh always called this his 'George Washington rifle,' " Gordon said with a grin.

"The George Washington rifle was then test fired," Gordon continued. "Marshall loaded the box magazine (the magazine held ten rounds). I was given pencil, paper, a tack and a homemade hammer with instructions to go to the target at the grape arbor, which was measured one hundred yards from the shop. I was to mark off the holes in the target as they were shot. Having full confidence in Marsh's shooting abilities, I stood about an arm's length from the target. Marsh began firing. At the end of five rounds the shooting stopped. I yelled, 'Shoot again.' Marsh yelled back, 'Something's wrong. Come to the shop.'

"I didn't know if the weapon had blown up or what, and I ran back to the shop. Marsh was in a quandry as to why he had fired only five times and yet he was out of ammunition. I suggested that he might have loaded only five rounds in the magazine. 'Hell no, I loaded ten rounds!' Marshall exclaimed. Marshall and I began to look for the empty cartridges on the floor and to our astonishment we found five empty and five live rounds. The realization came to Marsh instantly that his rifle was operating so violently that it was rebounding; in other words, it would fire one round, eject the empty, reload a fresh round and rebound again, ejecting the fresh round and again reload. In other words, it was firing every other round.

"There was no alternative," Gordon concluded, "Marsh had to make another and smaller chamber. This corrected the situation. The results of this thirty-day effort was the perfection of the now-world-famous Remington Model 550."

Weapons expert Gil Paust, in his article, "Rifles — The World's Six Best," published in the November 1956 issue of *Sportsman* magazine, explained the bewilderment of the shopper in trying to select the best rifle for his specific type of hunting. Having observed such a shopper, Paust decided to categorize the six best rifles, based on use. Included in his selection is the Remington Model 550 .22 rifle, which is marked "Williams's Patent" and utilizes the floating chamber. The popularity of this weapon was pointed out by Paust:

Through the years one rifle has become conspicuous above all others. It has had by far the greatest sale, over

1,000,000 having been marketed since its introduction in 1941, in spite of the fact that its production was discontinued during the war years of 1942-43. It is the Remington Model 550 A. [See Photos 26 and 27.]

This little gun is unique among .22's. If you don't own one, you've probably used one in a shooting gallery. It is an autoloading repeater with a tubular magazine holding 15 long rifle, 17 long or 22 short cartridges. Its weight is only 6¼ pounds and it is moderate in cost. The amazing feature of this autoloader is that it handles the various .22 cartridges without adjustment. This is made possible by the patented short chamber which 'floats' in the barrel, recoiling with the cartridge case when a short is fired, and thus supplying enough push to work the bolt and loading mechanism. When a long or short rifle cartridge is fired, however, the longer case projects beyond the floating chamber and locks it. Thus the action really is two-in-one. It works by the 'power piston' principle when shorts are used, and the conventional 'blow-back' system when handling longer cartridges.

The best small game and 'fun rifle,' so named by a million shooters in a relatively short number of years, is this .22 caliber Remington Model 550 A. This rifle is one of the many inventions by Carbine Williams that utilizes his world famous floating chamber, a new principle in firearms.

As you opened the door to Carbine's shop, you immediately encountered a huge precision milling machine standing dead-center in the entranceway. Knowing that Carbine had made most of his own tools, I became curious as to how and from where he had acquired this impressive piece of equipment.

"Ross, I was shipped this big, beautiful milling machine by Remington Arms Company. I was on a retainer by them. It came on a special rail car and was unloaded on a siding near here, brought to the shop and placed as you see it now. I developed one of my most unusual weapons on this machine for Remington. The mechanism of this weapon operated by the slight bulging of the shell head. This slight bulge had enough operating energy to operate

Photo 29. "It's just as easy to hit as it is to miss," Carbine said matter-of-factly. Again and again he proved to be the master shot, as it evidenced here. The shots penetrating the bull's eye are his—those on the outer perimeter are the author's.

Photo 30. "They called this the 'Impossible Shotgun' [the Model 50]. It is perfectly balanced and made a bunch of money for Winchester. This is the original, handmade model, and you can see where I shifted pins around here and there to improve my invention," Carbine explained.

the shotgun. Remington was afraid that the public would be skeptical about this method of operation, so it was dropped. The shotgun had a stationary barrel. I don't know whatever became of that model I made." Carefully cleaning up some spilled cigarette ashes, he said, "I guess that Remington still has it. Later on, on this same machine, I developed the Remington Model 550 .22 caliber rifle."

Winchester Model 50 — The "Impossible" Shotgun

With a hefty slap on the back, and showing more than routine interest in the subject, Carbine informed me one Saturday morning that we were going to talk about—and if I was real good, we would shoot—his Model 50 Winchester shotgun. From a rather battered shotgun case, Carbine brought forth the weapon.

"I crawled around under the damned kiln at Winchester and went through over a thousand pieces of wood before I found the one with the grain I wanted," Carbine said with a big smile. "I did my own finishing on this metal too—she's a beauty for sho', REB."

Prior to a delightful morning of shooting (though I was constantly outshot), Carbine related these interesting facts concerning the problems he had getting this particular weapon approved by the government for production and sale.

"When I first built this shotgun, the Model 50 (Photo 30), you wouldn't believe the problems I encountered. As you know, it utilized my floating chamber and was an entirely new concept in automatic shotguns. Well, before I got it introduced to Winchester good, the Alcohol, Tobacco, Tax and Firearms people descended on me claiming that it was, because of the floating chamber, a sawed-off shotgun that required registration under the Machine Gun Acts. We had one hell of a discussion about this, but eventually, when they understood the principle, they allowed this shotgun to go into production," he said, shaking his head as he remembered with contempt another of the many governmental roadblocks that had been thrown in his path.

"It is really a unique weapon, Ross," he continued. "It was the first shotgun in the history of firearms that was automatic, but with a nonrecoiling barrel. It's revolutionary in design, streamlined, perfectly balanced and brings a new standard of excellence in an automatic (self-loading) shotgun to the shooter. The Model 50 is the only shotgun in the world combining a nonrecoiling barrel and an independent chamber (my floating chamber).

"The chamber, bolt and inertia rod move together less than one-tenth of an inch when the gun is fired, starting the inertia rod on its way, through the cycle of unlocking the bolt, extracting and ejecting the empty shell, reloading, and locking the bolt. I eliminated the long-stroke recoil of conventional automatics. This streamlined shotgun shooting. The action is so instantaneous and smooth that your second shot is not distorted. I greatly reduced the recoil, which adds to shooting comfort and accuracy. One important feature of my Model 50 is the ease of dismantling for cleaning." With his huge and powerful hands, he swiftly disassembled the Model 50. "It is simplicity itself as far as design is concerned," he pointed out.

"As you know," Carbine continued, "you can buy and interchange barrels quickly and easily without special tools or factory fitting. It is also the only self-loading shotgun made that can be equipped with a ventilated rib with an unbroken sighting plane. My Model 50 is made in all gauges and it is a very popular shotgun for hunters and gun lovers. Later on they came out with the Model 59, which utilized the same principle, but they went to fiberglass barrels, which I did not particularly like."

World's Fastest Firing Machine Gun

Having worked very closely with Carbine in the introduction of his incredibly fast-firing machine gun and being thoroughly familiar with his expressed opinion that this weapon should be light and easily hand carried by a

178

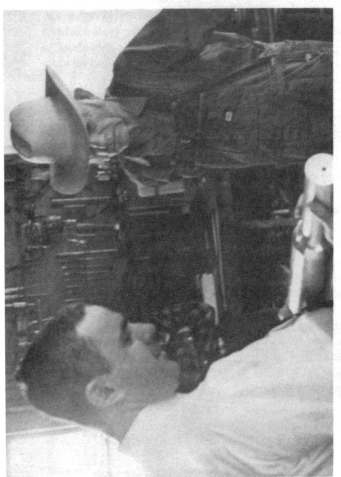

Photo 31. In the author's hands is the initial work done by the inventor in producing the first machine gun that fired two thousand rounds per minute. This was made by the inventor in his shop near Godwin, N.C., on his own equipment and with his own handmade tools.

Photo 32. "What the hell do you expect, REB? When you fire two thousand rounds a minute you can expect plenty of brass to police up." This was the first time that Williams had allowed the author to test fire the new machine gun. Rigid safety and policing procedures were always followed.

Photo 33. This was a test firing at Godwin just days before a visit to Fort Gordon, Georgia. The old grinding stone in the background was a treasured antique from Carbine's past. Often, when shooting from the shop window, Carbine would say, "Careful, REB. Don't hit the grind rock."

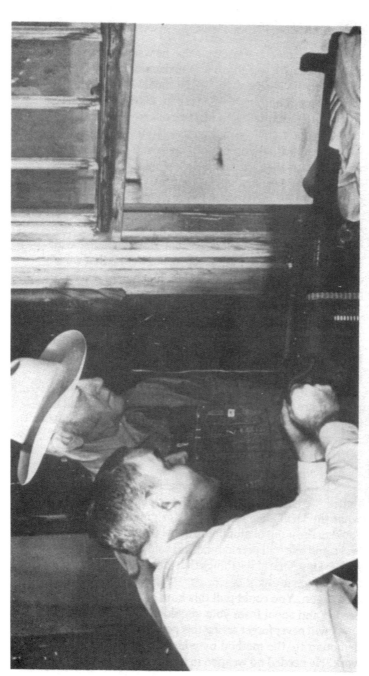

Photo 34. During the preliminary testing of Williams' machine gun, the author had the pleasure and excitement of firing this new weapon from the shop window.

single foot soldier (and knowing that he was totally capable of building such a weapon), I was anxious for him to explain to me why he designed the initial model with obviously greater length and increased weight. Carbine explained immediately that he would have preferred to build this initial weapon shorter and to use lighter-weight alloys where practical, but on meeting with and discussing his weapon with the Ordnance Department staff, those in authority were of the opinion that his weapon would be more favorably received by the military if it were more compatible with the size and weight of the regular .30 caliber Browning water-cooled machine gun.

"They wanted to see my machine gun compatible with the old and heavier Browning, REB, so I built it that way," Carbine explained. "In other words, I had in mind a light, fast-firing portable weapon easily handled by one foot soldier and they had in mind something similar to a machine gun then in use on a tank."

Referring again to taped interviews with Williams the following is his discussion of his new machine gun (Photos 31, 32, 33 and 34).

"All the Ordnance Department staff wanted it to weigh more and wanted it to be longer, but what I had in mind was to cut the barrel down to, say, about twelve inches, and that gives it about all the velocity in a .22 cartridge. In that case it wouldn't be but about eighteen inches long, the whole gun.

"In place of it being an all-steel gun," Carbine continued, "to have it heavy enough for tripod use, which was what the Ordnance Department originally wanted, we could make it out of aluminum alloy. It would run around seven and one-half pounds and, as I said, be about eighteen inches long. One of the things that makes it so effective, in addition to cutting it down, you'd have a stock like on a grease gun. You could pull this kind of stock back when needed and shoot from your shoulder."

I will never forget seeing this powerful man so vividly demonstrate the method by which his new idea would work. He needed no weapon in his hands to demonstrate the overall operation. I "saw" his idea come to life in my mind's eye.

"The [other] thing that would make it so effective is the cyclic rate of fire," Carbine continued. "It has two rates of fire: One is around a thousand a minute and the other is around two thousand a minute. You can adjust it from one rate of fire to another just like working the safety on a gun. The aluminum alloy would cut the weight down just about where you'd want it so you could shoot it easily from the shoulder or from the hip. It would be highly effective for close range due to the terrific rate of fire. At the present time, it's a .22 long rifle cartridge, high speed.

"We're figuring on making new models using all aluminum alloy, which is easy," he continued. "It has nothing to do with the working of the gun and we will use a .22 magnum cartridge with a full-patch bullet. This would double the energy and give about two thousand feet a second velocity. It would be highly effective for short ranges of from two to three hundred yards."

"Now, Carbine, in designing this new model, you were talking about the ammunition canister or container," I reminded him.

"Oh yes. You would have containers that would hold about two hundred fifty to three hundred cartridges in metallic disintegrated links made out of aluminum," he explained. "You'd clip the aluminum containers right on the side of the gun. You'd pull it open just like you would an aluminum beer can, then you'd snap it right on the side and just fire it from your shoulder. You'd shoot it just like you would a rifle. In order to carry it, you'd have a Sam Browne belt and holster and you'd carry it just like you would a pistol. It's like a side arm."

As our discussion continued and as we examined every unique aspect of this new weapon, I could see and feel the excitement building in Carbine. We were "talking his language"; the deep feelings he had for this weapon, and the vast knowledge pertaining to it, simply poured from his lips, mind and heart. Anxious to verify every possible point, I said: "One of the advantages we discussed is the fact that there is really no development time going to lapse since the basic weapon is already completed."

"No. No, the gun's all finished," he affirmed. "It went through Aberdeen Proving Ground without a malfunction. The only thing would be the adaptation of a new model to the magnum cartridge. We'd just make another gun, chambered for the .22 magnum. You wouldn't have to change anything hardly, just the throw of the bolt to give you more stroke in order to feed and do the necessary things."

"How long would it take you to make one of these aluminum models?" I asked.

"Well, I don't know." He hesitated. "That in itself for one man is a hell of a job."

"Well, suppose, Carbine, that you were taken to, say Colt or Remington, whomever you decided, and suppose they put at your disposal tool and die makers to follow your instructions to make this. What do you think it would take to make it?" I inquired.

"Well," Carbine paused, then continued, "it'd be a matter of some months. The first thing you'd want to do is to measure the pieces and make a blueprint of all the pieces so everybody could go to work at the same time. It's no job at all to make the drawing. You'd turn the drawing over to the model makers and they'd go right ahead and make the pieces."

"Barring any unforeseen circumstances, you say in five to six months you could probably make a model of it," I said in an effort to establish a more definite period of time.

"Oh, yes. And this gun has been tested at Fort Benning in Georgia, too. It went through all the tests. I think the functional test at Aberdeen was five thousand rounds. If you get the right kind of ammunition it won't malfunction. You got to have good strong ammunition," he emphasized.

"If you build this new model, you would pick just the right cartridge in the magnum caliber," I interjected.

"Oh, yes, in the magnum caliber," he agreed, "but the only reason you'd do that is to give it more power. It wouldn't make the gun any heavier at all. As far as the weight of the ammunition, it makes very little difference."

In making a comparison between the weight of the present military cartridge and the one proposed for Carbine's new machine gun, I said: "Carbine, if they utilized your light-weight machine gun and your new, lighter and smaller cartridge, our soldiers could surely carry more ammunition into combat than they presently carry, couldn't they?"

"Hell, yes!" Carbine exclaimed with a vehement smash of his fist against the surface of his workbench. He further pointed out that a greater quantity of ammunition could be carried in a smaller space in helicopters and on planes, in addition to the lower weight factor.

"It's the same weight of bullet," Carbine added, "but just a little longer. A long rifle cartridge is a forty-grain bullet and a magnum is also forty grain," he explained. "The cartridge is just a little longer and a little more powerful, that's all."

"But by developing this weapon, as compared to what the Army is using now, they would be able to carry a lot more of your ammunition and a lot lighter weapon," I said presumptively.

"Yes! The point is, you just couldn't live in a hail of fire at a cyclic rate of two thousand. Not even a long rifle at short range—you just couldn't live in it. You couldn't even hide from it," he emphasized. "It'd be like I trying to hide from hail.

"You could put any number of rounds of ammunition that you wanted to, depending on the use," Carbine continued. "You could put two hundred, five hundred, or even a thousand. If you got ready to walk with it, you'd shove the stock in and put it in the holster. You fire it exactly like you would a rifle. It wouldn't be near as heavy as an M-1 rifle. The point is the M-1 weighs pretty close to ten pounds, some of them a shade over with the right kind of wood. It would be at least two pounds lighter than the M-1 rifle. But that rate of fire is what I'm getting at. You could just wither 'most anything."

"Do you think this would be particularly effective in jungle-type warfare?" I questioned.

"Oh yes, of course," Carbine responded. "Any type where you're close. It wouldn't have to be jungle. The thing they need is short-range, maximum firepower and this is what this gun will give them. Now this model we've got here is a one-of-a-kind model. The mechanism is different from the other .22 machine guns but the principle is the same. They all have the movable chamber. That's the thing that makes 'em go. Without that they wouldn't do anything, nothing at all. This model was never adopted. The only model that was adopted was the old model."

"And the Ordnance Department was primarily concerned then in using up parts they had. So this gun is an entirely different thing," I added.

"Yes, the first .22 machine gun adopted was the U.S. Machine Gun caliber .22 M-1 — in 1933," he recalled after a slight hesitation.

"So everybody that was associated with it then has forgotten about it?" I asked.

"That's right. Now the need is different. The jungle warfare, the short range, the light ammunition is the need today. I made all the models. There was six of them all together for issue to the using services. I think Washington Ordnance Department wanted one at Springfield Armory. The vote was unanimous for adoption. There was nobody that didn't think well of it.

"Of course, I was at the Springfield Armory quite a bit during the blueprint stages and manufacturing," Williams continued. "The Ordnance Department told Springfield Armory they were not to do anything to that gun but make it. They usually had a habit of fiddling with something if they got a hold of it. They said, 'Don't do anything with that gun but make it.' Because it'd proved itself. And that's the way it was made. To change this gun, you don't have to do much to it. You just cut the barrel off and use whatever aluminum you can in place of steel. Then it won't be but about the length of a carbine."

"I read recently that they were making some parts out of fiberglass. What do you think of that?" I asked, suppressing a grin with difficulty.

"No! Hell, no! I'm no fiberglass man! Damn fiberglass!" Carbine literally screamed out. "I want it to be made out of metal, and if it needs a certain stock it be wood. If a skeleton stock is needed, it should be made out of metal."

"Carbine, you know another adaptation you could make on that gun—just as a thought—there might be a possibility of adapting a folding stock similar to your carbine stock," I suggested.

"Well, sure, you could do that," he agreed. "It don't make no difference, a folding stock or a skeleton stock. It's been the opinion for years—of course, I couldn't foresee and didn't think of it—but people in authority in Washington thought that it would be a good gun for civil disturbances. I don't believe I even talked about it. Well, every police and sheriff's department would want one of these light models. Everyone! You couldn't keep them from getting 'em. It ain't a matter of Vietnam. The demands from the police and sheriffs' offices could warrant the manufacture. These people in Washington (I don't like to call no names) thought the reason that it would be so good for civil disturbances is that you wouldn't be shooting at people a mile away. You'd be shooting at people immediate to you."

At this point Carbine offered to allow us to fire a few belts so that my guests could see the awesome firepower of this little weapon. We readily agreed. Our firing a hundred rounds in three seconds (thirty-three and one-third rounds per second) sounded like someone rapidly ripping a short piece of canvas into strips.

After firing this weapon numerous times, you suddenly became aware of the fact that you were hearing three simultaneous-but-distinct sounds. First, you heard the sound of the hundred rounds being fired; next, you actually heard the impact of the projectiles; and finally, you heard the expended brass hitting the ground. No words can adequately describe the firepower or the feeling one has as this weapon performs. It is mechanical perfection and, sincerely, it is like stepping twenty years into the future. There is no weapon in military use today that comes close to the performance for firepower of this machine gun.

It was exciting enough to me, a seasoned gun collector, to fire this weapon, but to my guests, many of whom had never even seen a machine gun — or who, at best, had fired once or twice the standard military models — it was to be an unforgettable experience. Williams began swiftly setting up his machine gun for the firing demonstration. Directing every step of the preparations (and abruptly ordering several of us out of his way), Carbine suggested that my guests might like to have a souvenir target. To their delight, Carbine set up a wooden frame, placed ten sheets of cardboard approximately twenty-four inches square, one over the other, noting that by firing through all ten sheets at the same time, each would have an identical target. After a moment's thought, he further suggested that we all autograph the targets following the firing. These targets are treasured possessions and are proudly displayed in dens in North and South Carolina.

"Now she's ready to fire. She's ready to roll. Get hold to her," Carbine instructed. "Fire away any time you want." We fired one hundred rounds. "O.K.! Do you want to look at the target?" he asked. "Let's go down and take a look at it."

"That's the greatest weapon that's ever been built as far as I'm concerned. Not a damn thing can touch it!" I exclaimed.

Preparing for a second one hundred-round firing, Carbine said, "I'll try one short burst for sighting purposes." A short burst was fired. "Did we hit it?"

At the precise moment we prepared to fire, Miss Spot, Carbine's dog, ran directly in front of the machine gun.

"Damn! Watch the dog!"

"Where's the dog?"

"It's all right. I'll watch her." Carbine added a precaution: "If I put my hand on your shoulder, stop shooting. Are you ready?"

"Yeah, man."

"Fire!"

We shot Remington high-speed long rifle ammunition with a .22 lead bullet. The penetration was impressive. It went through a two-by-four with no effort at all, and dug up the dirt on the other side. Another burst went through both one-inch legs of a saw horse.

Scheduling a demonstration of a machine gun for the government is no easy task. During 1965 and well into 1966, I worked almost daily trying to persuade the U.S. Government to let the inventor demonstrate his machine gun, or at least to have someone in authority examine it. I had very little success. I have more than three hundred pieces of frustrating correspondence demonstrating that my requests were received and forwarded again and again to various persons who were not remotely interested in, or, in fact, involved in, weapons development.

A typical example of this ridiculous buck passing was a letter received from the space agency regretfully advising that they had no known use at this time for a machine gun that would fire two thousand rounds a minute. I could not help but agree, but I quickly add that not once did we write, or remotely suggest, that they might have such a use.

Finally, through the help of a close Camden, South Carolina, friend, W. W. Wannamaker, III, we were able to get an expression of genuine interest in the weapon from General William Westmoreland. Simultaneously, we contacted, and were given great assistance in setting up a firing demonstration, by General Hugh Pate Harris, then commandant of The Citadel in Charleston, South Carolina.

Just one week prior to our planned departure for Fort Benning for the firing demonstration, to our dismay, we received a curt and threatening letter from the Federal Alcohol, Tobacco, Tax and Firearms Department, notifying us that it was illegal to manufacture a machine gun, illegal to know or associate with anyone that would do so, illegal to transport said weapon, and *absolutely* forbidden when the builder and transporter was an ex-convict. But thanks to South Carolina Senator Strom Thurmond and some high officials within ATTF who had served in South Carolina, the ATTF consented to allow us to transport the machine gun, and to demonstrate it for the Army in compliance with General Westmoreland's request and General Harris' arrangements.

We faced approximately a hundred and fifty weapons experts at Fort Benning, headed by General Robert H. York, commanding general. Shooting with us was one of America's top machine gunners, a Master Sergeant Hendrick. He watched Carbine Williams fire a belt of a hundred rounds in three seconds and then he fired a belt of a hundred rounds. Sitting back on his heels, Sergeant Hendrick smiled and said to General York, "Sir, don't show me any more. Just get me one of them."

General York and other officials fired the weapon and seemed delighted with its performance and possibilities. Following the shooting demonstration, Carbine and I faced the audience for a question-and-answer period.

"Mr. Williams, which part breaks the most often?" General York began the interrogation.

Williams, slightly deaf, asked me what the general said. I repeated the question and Williams replied, "General I can't answer that question. I never, ever broke a part."

The general patiently rephrased his question. "Mr. Williams, in preparation for this demonstration, what spare part did not make the largest number of?"

A booming response followed: "God almighty, General, if I'd thought this weapon was gonna fly apart, I wouldn't have come here! I've fired over thirty-eight thousand rounds through her and I ain't never made a spare part." (Photo 35)

"Mr. Williams," General York inquired in obvious amazement, "you are telling me that you came for this demonstration today before these experts and never made or brought one spare part or a second weapon?"

"That's what I'm a telling you, General. She has fired over thirty-eight thousand rounds and I defy you to show

Photo 35. "God almighty, General. If I'd thought this weapon was gonna fly apart I wouldn't have come here! I've fired over thirty-eight thousand rounds through her and I ain't never made a spare part," Williams exclaimed during a test firing of his machine gun at Fort Benning in November 1965.

Photo 36. "Gentlemen, I have fired over 38,000 rounds through this weapon without a malfunction or misfire. I have never replaced a part and there is no evidence of wear to any part or the barrel," Carbine said to amazed Ordnance experts.

me evidence of stress or wear on any part, including the barrel." (Photo 36)

This brought a standing ovation from those listening to the exchange between the two men. Later one official commented to me that had this been a demonstration by an arms company, they would have had ten weapons, fourteen technical representatives, ten cases of spare parts and a million preprinted excuses for every possible malfunction.

Further along in the exchange, in reply to a question from one of the experts in the stands, Williams explained, "Gentlemen, this machine gun has malfunctioned once, and it is witnessed and recorded as a failure on the part of the ammunition and not the weapon." When asked about the ammunition used for this demonstration, Williams again astonished the crowd by saying, "Oh, we stopped on the way down and bought four cases of cartridges from a local hardware store."

The experts could not believe that this was "store-bought" commercial ammunition rather than specially prepared factory loads. They were further astonished when Williams demonstrated that the belt feed mechanism was so strong that, by holding the belt as it was being fed through the machine gun, you could pull the weapon over without causing a malfunction.

Top weapons and Ordnance experts there were also fascinated and delighted that the cartridges being fed at such a rapid rate through the weapon were regular soft, lead-tipped .22 ammunition, and that they were fed from a fabric belt under wet weather conditions, which usually makes cloth belt feed very difficult. They could hardly believe that this weapon was not firing on contact but was, in fact, hammer-fired.

As was so often the case, very favorable reports were written and a number of articles were published, but no effort was made to accept or even test the weapon further. Again, Williams was way ahead of his time with his weapon.

On returning to Godwin and hearing nothing more from the military, Carbine Williams commented. "Well, Ross, she will be one hell of a bird gun here on the old farm."

The internal mechanism from the machine gun is safely secured in the hands of the Williams family now. The beautiful and deadly little machine gun itself is displayed in the center of Williams' shop, now relocated in the North Carolina Department of Archives and History Building in Raleigh. Someday someone in the military is going to realize what Williams invented, and his name, in memory this time, will resurface as a leader in weapons design and development.

T-3 Carbine

During my many visits with Carbine Williams during our association, we often discussed the various kinds of carbines that were produced, the different models and the different variations. It was during one of these conversations that we decided that it would be interesting to collect from all over the United States at least one model of each of these carbines.

I proceeded to do this and through countless letters, numerous trips and extensive contacts through gun shows and fellow gun collectors, I was able to acquire one of every known model of the carbine with the exception of two. One which I have never found is marked Singer and was manufactured for a limited time by Singer Sewing Machine Company. The other that I lacked was a carbine called the T-3, of which we found only two hundred and fifty-two models were made. "Ross, I don't reckon you'll ever find one of those," Carbine lamented.

Despite his pessimism, I persisted for two years in my attempt to locate one of these weapons. I was unsuccessful. However, I was delighted when a friend brought me one-half of a receiver from one of these carbines. Although it had been cut in half by a welding torch when the guns were being salvaged, I was still excited that we had at least found a part which would verify their production.

I dashed up to Carbine's shop, walked in, and excitedly proclaimed, "Look what I've got!" Carbine took this piece of rather rusty, badly cut metal in his hands and said with not a trace of excitement, "Ross, what in the hell are you gonna do with this."

"Damn it!" I said, "I've been looking for it for two years and I'm going to include it in our collection of carbines."

Without another word of discussion, Carbine Williams walked over to his window and flung the piece of metal as far as he could throw it into the field. I nearly had a fit. When I finished protesting, Carbine said calmly, "I don't know what the hell you are worried about. They made two hundred and fifty-six of these."

I said, "No, you're incorrect. They made two hundred and fifty-two."

"No, Ross, *you're* incorrect, and so are the records. I was in on this," he said. "Come with me."

We walked across the field to his now-famous smokehouse (Photo 37) in which he housed hundreds of parts and all of his extremely rare handmade guns. After rummaging through a trunk for a while, Carbine produced a barrel, a trigger assembly, a stock and other pieces. Finally, almost ceremoniously, he lifted from one of the trunks the receiver of a T-3.

He smiled, winked at me and said, "Ross, I just wanted to see if you were really interested in getting one. You see, they made two hundred and fifty-six of them and I have the other four. They have never been assembled and I'm gonna make you one today."

The following conversation took place April 29, 1967, in Carbine Williams' shop when he assembled the T-3.

"Carbine, what are you making?" I asked, to establish the identity of the weapon being assembled.

"Damn it, I'm trying to put one of these crazy carbines together — you know, the T-3."

"That's about the rarest one there is," I suggested. "Well, that's pretty skilled work, isn't it?"

Photo 37. This ordinary-looking building, a former smokehouse, housed for years many of Williams' handmade inventor's models. If you opened the door, you stood the chance of getting a face full of 00 buckshot, for the room was "well guarded" against uninvited guests. All weapons are now in the North Carolina Department of Archives and History Building in Raleigh, and this building stands vacant.

"Oh yes. It takes an expert to do what I'm doing. It's gonna cost you like hell, too. I go by the hour," Carbine said straight-faced.

"What's your rate per hour?" I asked. "I'd better see if I can afford this work."

"$1.68 an hour."

"Great day! That's a pretty high price for unskilled labor, isn't it?" I joked.

"That's skilled labor," he retorted.

"Oh, that's skilled labor. Well then, you think it'd take an expert to do that?"

"It sure does. I don't know whether we're ever gonna get it together or not from the looks of it. You have to do some real fine work to put it together." After working with the parts awhile, Carbine continued, "Well now, I believe I'm gonna have to work on the shoulder a little bit, the barrel shoulder."

"You put me on about that T-3 receiver, you know," I chided him. "I worked about two years to try and find one and I found a half receiver only, and then you turn up with an original Winchester."

"Sure did. Here it is! We've got to go and get a piston and a retainer though," Carbine said. "It is not a *nut,* it's a *retainer* for the piston."

"Remember what you told me about that fellow who called the retainer a 'nut'?" I asked.

"He worked for me," Carbine said. "Who in the hell ever saw a nut with the threads on the outside? It's a bushing. It's a retainer bushing for the piston."

"You classified *him* when you called it that, didn't you?" I kidded.

"Yeah. He's the nut."

"Carbine, what are you doing now?" I inquired.

"Cleaning up the piston and the piston retainer."

"Those are some mighty sophisticated tools you're using there," I continued kidding him, taking advantage of this rare occasion when he was in a frivolous mood.

"Yes, a toothpick, toothbrush and gasoline!" Carbine said, obviously enjoying the repartee.

"Well, I guess that's what skilled people use. You just have to have the best."

"Oh yes, you have to have the best," he agreed with a grin.

At this point Carbine was installing the piston and the Winchester barrel of the T-3. He completed the assembly and testing of the rifle the same day. When he finished zeroing this rifle, it was not only a beauty to look at, but one of the most accurate carbines in my collection, and certainly a unique one. He autographed this weapon for me, and in the stock cut where the sling normally goes, applied with his own die, his mark of proof.

Development of the M-1 Carbine

In 1940 Marshall Williams became overnight an internationally known leader in the field of weapons inventions.

The Army had taken the .32 Winchester self-loading cartridge and made modifications, which in turn had led to the development of a cartridge called the caliber .30 SRM-1 (caliber .30 semirimmed M-1). This was again altered to become the carbine .30 M-1 cartridge. As is so often the case, the Army had developed the cartridge and had announced that it would hold firings to test a rifle that would utilize this cartridge. A stipulation was that the rifle must not weigh more than five and one-half pounds.

The response was overwhelming. Every would-be inventor and many major gun companies entered the competition in hopes of securing a lucrative government contract. Amazingly enough, Winchester Arms Company, for which Williams was then working, at first did not plan to enter the competition. They were occupied with producing the M-1 Garand, and they were attempting to develop a rising block .30-'06 rifle for the Marine Corps, based on an invention of Marshall Williams. About this time, however, the Marine Corps' interest in this weapon waned due to the ever-increasing possibility of war. When Winchester Arms Company received a second call from the government reminding it of the competition, it dropped the Marine project and made preparations to enter it.

There are conflicting stories concerning the development of the weapon submitted to the Ordnance Department. Winchester would claim that "teamwork" was responsible for the development of the M-1 carbine it entered. Possibly, to a great degree, teamwork in the form of rapidly produced parts and other similar work was the reason for Winchester's being able to design, build, complete, test, enter and win the competition, *only fifteen days after it decided to compete.* But, from a review of the patents held by Marshall Williams for every conceivable part of the rifle—from the barrel band to the heart of the carbine to the short-stroke piston—it is my belief that it was, indeed, Carbine Williams who carried the ball all the way for Winchester during this development.

The deadline for competition entry was September 15, 1941. On Saturday morning, September 13, 1941, the Winchester carbine was completed and taken out for final testing. On that very Saturday morning, Winchester received word that the deadline had been moved up to Sunday, September 14. Winchester had less than twenty-four hours to test this new carbine through a one-thousand-round firing before submitting it to Ordnance.

Testing began almost immediately. However, the carbine started jamming and at times would not fire at all. Williams concluded that the piston was not receiving sufficient gas. This could be corrected simply by drilling the gas port larger, he concluded. One small hitch: no one knew now much larger it should be. Yet, they could not afford to be wrong, for they only had one barrel and no time remaining to make another.

The gas port was at an angle, making additional drilling difficult, and on the initial attempt they broke off the drill tip in the gas port. As one man very carefully removed the broken drill, others quickly built a device that would hold the barrel in a rigid position for further drilling. The gas port was then slightly and carefully enlarged. On reassembly the weapon operated perfectly.

During the discussion of how much larger this port should be, Carbine's response to his mechanics and management at Winchester was, "Hell, I don't know how large it should be. I ain't never seen one before like this. I just invented it."

Clip after clip of carbine ammunition was run through this weapon and the test was successful beyond every expectation. Edwin Pugsley, then director of research and design for Winchester, later recalled, "It is doubtful that any group of men ever became so enthusiastic in so short a period and you can bet your boots Williams was in there pitching. The gas piston was his idea and it worked."

The Winchester carbine was entered in competition the next day and won out over all other entries. Winchester received a contract from the goernment for this weapon that was worth, in the beginning, more than $800,000. This carbine was later to be produced in larger quantities than any other weapon in the world. The best records available indicate that well over eight million were made, plus millions upon millions of spare parts produced for repair and/or replacement.

Contrary to popular belief, Carbine Williams did not receive a royalty on every carbine that was produced. Various magazines and newspapers carried articles indicating that the exact price was secret, and one article referred to him as the man who was handed a million dollars in cash. In reality, Marshall Williams received a total of $250,000 for his invention. Later the government contracted with a number of other companies to produce the M-1 carbine and variations of it such as the M-1A1, M-2 and M-3, and Williams received no royalties from these.

To confirm the statement made as to the variety of companies that manufactured the carbine, detailed is a report provided by the Office of the Chief of Military History, Department of the Army, Washington, D.C., prepared by Harry C. Thomson and Lida Mayo.

The Carbine Enters the Picture

One of the most popular items or ordnance used by American troops in World War II was the lightweight carbine. Designed to replace the automatic pistol for certain purposes, it was intended primarily as a defensive weapon for service troops, but it also appealed to combat infantrymen as a companion weapon for the more powerful Garand, and was affectionately nicknamed 'baby Garand.' Fully loaded with a 15-cartridge magazine and with sling attached, it weighed less than six pounds and was about three feet long. It was fairly accurate at ranges up to three hundred yards—at least four times the effective range of the pistol. A gas operated, semiautomatic weapon, the carbine followed some of the design principles of the Garand, but with certain distinctive features. By definition, a carbine is a light rifle with a short barrel, commonly used during the nineteenth century by mounted troops. Early in the twentieth century, carbines passed out of the picture in the United States as the Springfield rifle, adopted in 1903, proved satisfactory for both mounted and foot troops. But by the 1940's aircraft, tanks, and new infantry weapons had brought about marked changes in military tactics. Cavalry was no longer as important as it had been, but new elements with greater mobility had come on the scene with the result that flanks and rear areas, including airfields, were under constant threat of air or mechanized attack. At the same time, the addition to small infantry units of such weapons as machine guns, trench mortars, and anti-tank guns brought the need for an auxiliary offensive-defensive weapon for the soldiers who manned them or carried ammunition for them. The pistol was ideal for combat at point-blank range. It was issued to officers, to troops manning crew-served weapons, and to rear area service troops, but few soldiers could hit anything with it beyond twenty-five yards. As a full-size rifle was unnecessarily heavy for such troops, the carbine seemed to be the answer.

The Infantry, as early as 1938, had asked that Ordnance develop a .30-caliber carbine weighing five pounds or less, and with an accuracy range of three hundred yards. Ordnance objected on the ground that such a weapon would require special ammunition. But the infantry pressed its demand, and in the fall of 1940 a definite requirement was set up for a weapon of this type. Thereafter events moved with bewildering speed. Ordnance requested Winchester, which had extensive experience with ammunition for semiautomatic weapons, to undertake design of a cartridge for the proposed carbine. Modeled on an existing Winchester .32 caliber cartridge, the new carbine ammunition was submitted in November 1940, found satisfactory, and approved for production in small experimental lots.

Meanwhile Ordnance had sent a circular to gun manufacturers and designers throughout the country inviting submission of model weapons for preliminary engineering tests. Of the nine models presented for trial in the summer of 1941, three did not meet the general specifications and were withdrawn, leaving six models actually tested. Though all showed promise, none was entirely satisfactory. As a result of the tests, the Ordnance Committee dropped the requirement for full-automatic fire, deciding that the proposed carbine should be strictly semiautomatic. Two of the guns tested showed such promise that five toolroom models of each, embodying the improvements recommended after the tests, were ordered. One was the Bendix Aviation Corporation entry designed by George J. Hyde; the other was the Springfield Armory entry designed by John C. Garand. In August 1940, Hyde had become associated with the Inland Manufacturing Division of General Motors Corporation, and had constructed there the toolroom models of his design. At the same time, Inland signed a contract for preparation of production studies of both the Hyde and Garand models.

Since none of the models tested in May and June proved satisfactory, Ordnance extended the deadline until 15 September 1941, the date set for the final service tests. It urged inventors to improve and resubmit their guns, and invited designers who had not yet entered the contest to do so. In July 1941 Ordnance, impressed by an improved version of Winchester's semiautomatic rifle, asked Winchester to build a sample carbine of similar design. Fully occupied with production of the M-1 rifle and other development work, Winchester had not submitted a carbine for the earlier tests. But in just fourteen days after accepting Ordnance's invitation to construct a carbine, Winchester completed a handmade first model. Though not a finished product, it passed its preliminary tests at Aberdeen on 11 August 1941. There remained only thirty-four days for Winchester to perfect its design and complete an improved specimen for entry in the general service tests set for 15 September. After intensive day and night work that set a new record for weapon development, Winchester met the deadline.

All told, six models were entered in the September tests, including one each of the two designs that had earlier showed such promise that Ordnance had ordered toolroom models. The Winchester carbine out-performed them all. On 30 September 1941, exactly one year after Ordnance had first announced that a carbine was desired by the Army and only two months after Winchester had started work on its design, the Ordnance Committee recommended standardization of the Winchester model. This recommendation was formally approved on 22 October 1941, and the new weapon was given the designation carbine, caliber .30, M-1.

PRODUCTION CONTRACTS—Just as speed had keynoted development of the new weapon, speed became the goal for getting into production. The first requirement was set at 886,698, and funds were at once made available for procurement. Since Winchester's facilities were inadequate to turn out this number, Ordnance selected as a second contractor GMC's Inland Division, which had gained some knowledge of carbine manufacture through its production studies of the Hyde, Springfield, and Winchester models. Without waiting until an agreement could be worked out with the government regarding manufacturing rights, Winchester quickly agreed to share its knowledge with Inland. In November 1941, Ordnance placed large contracts with both Winchester and Inland for each to produce at the rate of one thousand per day. Soon thereafter Winchester assigned a license to the United States Government for production of M-1 carbines in exchange for a fee of $886,000.

POST-PEARL HARBOR REQUIREMENTS—Pearl Harbor found the United States with something over

1,600,000 rifles on hand, in depot stocks, and in the hands of troops, including state guards. They were mostly Springfields and Enfields, but included nearly 350,000 new Garands. The inventory also included about 480,000 pistols and revolvers, about 60,000 machine guns (mostly .30 caliber) and some 56,000 BAR's. During the hectic weeks that followed the attack on Pearl Harbor, Anglo-American planners drew up ambitious programs for procuring millions of additional small arms. In his message to Congress on 6 January 1942, President Roosevelt set the pace by listing requirements for one million machine guns of all kinds. In the Army's munitions program of February 1942, rifle requirements were set at four billion for the year 1942. The staggering total of twelve million rifles became the goal for production by June 1944. In addition, more than four million carbines were to be turned out during the same 30-month period, plus three and a half million pistols and five million submachine guns. The grand total was twenty-five million weapons. Only about one-third of the rifles were for the United States forces; the remaining two-thirds—over five million Springfields, nearly a million Garands, and over a million Enfields— were scheduled for lend-lease.

Even for some of the Army people those figures appeared high. The following exchange at the production conference on small arms in February 1942 illustrates the feeling of incredulity with which some planners viewed the post-Pearl Harbor requirements:

General Somervell: 'I would just like to ask a question. It may be terribly ignorant, but we set up for an American army of 10 million people, 528,000 of these machine guns. Now we are proposing to build 1,302,000 of them. In other words, it will be for an army of about 24 milllion people.'

Judge Patterson: 'What's this? Where do you get that figure?'

General Somervell: 'Take line three. . .God, I just don't believe it.'

General Aurand: 'I can explain it. . .About from 75 to 80 percent of the tanks that are on this program are Defense Aid tanks. . .If we are going to get the tanks. . .and other things that are in there, we are going to have these machine guns for them.'

General Moore: 'They are basing that on a lot of wastage, a lot of short life for tanks, and of course if a tank goes out, a machine gun goes with it. So it really isn't based on the number of men: it is based on the tanks.' And so on and on it went.

CARBINES — The ink had barely dried on the first two carbine contracts with Winchester and Inland in 1941 when the United States found itself at war. Before Pearl Harbor, requirements for carbines had stood at 886,698, but the War Munitions Program drawn up in February 1942 listed over one million needed by the end of 1942 and over three million by the end of 1943. As Winchester and Inland were being set up to produce only one thousand each per day and could not start producing at all before June, achievement of the one million goal for 1942 was clearly impossible for them. Part of the 1942 shortage could be offset by speeding production of Springfields and by issuing old Enfields in place of carbines, but for the future additional producers had to be lined up. As no single plant could meet the whole deficit, five smaller plants were placed under contract, each to turn out thirty thousand carbines per month. Known as the second wave of carbine plants, these were the Rock-Ola Company and Quality Hardware and Machine Company, both of Chicago; Irwin-Pederson Arms Company of Grand Rapids; Underwood-Elliot-Fisher Company of Hartford, Connecticut; and the Rochester Defense Corporation of Rochester, New York. Most were inexperienced in munitions making, having turned from making hardware, juke boxes, and typewriters; yet all but one proved successful.

No sooner had these five new producers been added than further expansion became necessary. By June 1942 carbine requirements had jumped to over four million needed by the end of 1943. In what was known as the third wave of expansion, a contract was awarded in August 1942 to Standard Products Company of Port Clinton, Ohio, for manufacture of carbines at the rate of forty-five thousand per month. Meanwhile, Inland had started producing in June, only six months after signing its contract, and by the end of the year reached a rate of one thousand per day. Winchester started producing in September, followed by

Underwood-Elliot-Fisher and Rock-Ola in November. Although the November 1942 Army Supply Program made deep cuts in most items, the drop in carbine requirements was slight and the need for additional producers again became apparent. In January and February 1943 contracts were placed with International Business Machine Corporation and Saginaw Steering Gear Division of General Motors Corporation, both of whom were nearing completion of orders for other types of small arms. This so-called fourth wave brought the total of carbine prime contractors to ten. Of this group, Inland, the first plant to start producing, became the leader, making available to other firms the details of its manufacturing techniques along with drawings and specifications for tools, jigs, and fixtures. Because of its close contacts with gage manufacturers, Inland was awarded a contract for procurement of gages for the entire carbine program. Of all the carbine contractors the only one that failed to produce was Irwin-Pederson. After this concern experienced many production problems Ordnance canceled the contract, purchased the company's plant at Grand Rapids, and arranged for Saginaw Steering to operate it.

INTEGRATION COMMITTEES — With so many contractors in the carbine picture the need for over-all coordination soon arose. In late March 1942 Ordnance called together representatives of the seven prime contractors, discussed production problems, and gradually worked out procedures for interchange of ideas, raw materials, and machine tools. At first called Carbine Production Committee, this group later took the name of industry integration committee, in common with other similar committees formed by the Ordnance Department. The carbine committee appears to have been the first such committee formed by the Ordnance Department with the mechanical time fuse committee a close second.

Carbine Variations

Some years ago I decided that I would try to locate and purchase every known model and variation of the carbine, and that I would ask Carbine to zero these pieces in and personally inspect, proof mark and autograph each weapon on the stock. This collection grew nicely and, like myself, Carbine was proud of the accomplishments we made in locating and assembling this rather outstanding collection.

Not one to leave room for error, Carbine suggested one day that it would be fitting to add to the collection at least one carbine that could not be duplicated or found on the market. After much deliberation, he decided that he would build from original experimental parts an unnumbered carbine. When time came for the assembly of this unique weapon (Photo 38), I turned on the tape recorder. The following conversation between the writer and the inventor concerns the assembly and testing of this one-of-a-kind carbine. (I must add that some months later, for my birthday, Carbine Williams presented me with a serial number "1" carbine, saying, "Now you have every known model of the carbine, plus serial numbers '0' and '1.' There's no damned way anyone will ever surpass this collection, and that's the way it should be." The serial number "1" carbine was assembled from experimental parts made at the time he was final-testing the carbine for Winchester.)

"This carbine I put together here for Ross Beard. . .is a 'no-name' carbine — no numbers or no name on it. It's got all the old parts, the first model marks, safety, magazine catch, rear sight and all the parts that go with the first model, including the cut in the stock for the oiler and the sling. It's all the old number one model." Carbine's evaluation was that "It shoots pretty good."

"What you think about it shooting 'pretty good'?" I asked. "You shot two rounds with it just now, didn't you, Carbine, and where did they hit?"

"Pretty nigh in the same hole," he conceded.

"This is exactly the same carbine designed as the one in this beautiful schematic drawing on your wall here?" I asked in an effort to authenticate the weapon he had assembled.

Photo 38. "It ain't quite as famous as the one I'm holding, REB, for mine is autographed by General MacArthur and many other celebrities, but yours was built by me for you from scratch, so I guess that counts for something. She shoots pretty damned good too," Carbine confessed.

"Oh yes, it's the same thing as the drawing," he verified, "but it don't have any numbers on it. It's one made from the old, original, experimental parts. No number on it yet."

"There are not any of those floating around are there, Carbine?" I asked.

"No, not that I know of."

"Boy, that's going to be a treasured part of my collection," I said in admiration. With this he laughed and gave me a solid punch to the chest.

"If I can ever get enough pieces, I might make *me* one." With this he laughed and gave me a solid punch to the chest.

"Well, you sport one or two low-number carbines and also one with a few right fancy signatures on it, don't you?" I asked.

"Oh, yes."

"I want you to show those to some of my friends in Camden someday."

"All right," he agreed.

To my delight, a few weeks later Carbine Williams and Miss Maggie arrived at my home in Camden. Their car was loaded down from trunk to front seat with an assortment of Carbine's inventor's models, knives he had made in prison, tools, handmade mallets and other interesting items. I had arranged for a number of close friends to come by to meet the couple. To my delight, Carbine took special interest in their children. Again and again he met groups of from five to twenty children and explained in detail the operation of each of his weapons. Several older boys brought their M-1 carbines by and he graciously autographed the stock of each weapon for them.

I once dared to suggest to Carbine that he might want to rest. That was a mistake. He was having a good time and had no intention of sitting down or resting, and told me so in no uncertain terms. For hours on end he greeted and personally conducted tours of his weapons, displayed throughout my living room. He signed autographs and posed again and again for photographs with children and for the local paper. He was the center of attention and he loved it. Those who had the pleasure of meeting Carbine and Miss Maggie loved it, too.

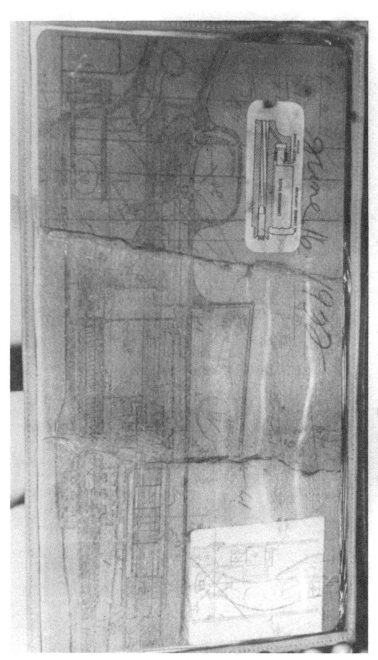

Photo 1-23   The conception drawing made while in prison of "Carbine's" rifles (R.E. Beard).

CHAPTER 9
Working with Winchester

In 1941, Winchester convinced Marshall Williams to come to work at its Connecticut plant. On the surface this sounds reasonable, for the usual method of inventing and building a weapon is for an inventor to work with a great team, to draw countless blueprints, and to have available a team of consultants and tool and die makers to handle his every need. Yes, teams and teamwork are the usual prerequisites for perfecting a new product in the weapons field. But Williams' manner was reserved, and certainly anyone who knew him recognized immediately that he was a loner when it came to inventing and building.

Like so many large corporations today, Winchester did not understand the quirks of genius. Company personnel knew of Williams' impressive inventions in the weapons field, but since Marshall Williams had completed only the eighth grade in school, had no engineering education and had but little knowledge of other firearms design development over the years, they felt the necessity to direct him. They sincerely felt that the thing to do to utilize best this man was to put someone in the office with Williams to write down everything he said or did. This, obviously, was a mistake.

Edwin Pugsley, director of research and design, decided to place another new employee, Harry Sefried, in the office with Williams. Sefried was instructed to remain close to Williams and write down his ideas and comments.

Sefried has since become successful in the weapons field (he became chief of pistol research with High Standard Manufacturing Corporation and later worked with Ruger on the .44 carbine), but he soon realized that he had a rough, if not impossible, road ahead of him at Winchester trying to "read and write down" Marshall Williams.

Both men were assigned to the same office in the rambling H-shaped building at Winchester. Like so many industrial workers, Sefried would arrive promptly at eight each morning and equip himself with pencil and paper. But if Williams was working on anything, the inventor would promptly slip it into his top drawer, lock it and sit back, arms folded, and not speak a word. This got on Sefried's nerves. After all, having been given an assignment, he felt he had to report some progress. But the sheet of paper intended to cover Williams' activities of the day included little more than each morning's greeting.

During the weeks of silence, Sefried had observed that ever so often Marshall would grasp in his vice-like hands one of the sixty-penny nails he kept in his desk and bend it into hairpin shape. One morning after Marsh had performed this trick, without a word Sefried reached over, grabbed up the bent spike and, holding cotton waste in each hand, straightened the nail. He put it down in front of Marsh and walked out without a word.

Sefried had set up this situation in advance. On leaving the office he rushed to a hole in the plaster board wall where he could observe the reaction which was sure to come. He saw Marsh pick up another spike that he had bent, grasp it with his handkerchief and damn near dismember his hands trying to straighten it as Sefried had done. He was not successful, but typical of Marshall Williams he put his mind to work to figure out how the feat had been accomplished. At length he reached over and patted the pile of waste that Harry had used to hold the spike. Burrowed in it were two short sections of .45 caliber pistol barrel.

Sefried returned shortly to the office. Not a word was spoken, but Marshall Williams had for the first time a twinkle in his eye. At the end of the day he gave Sefried a powerful slap in the middle of his back and asked, "Harry, what are you doing tonight?"

"Oh, nothing much, Marsh," Harry replied.

"Why don't you stop over to my place for a little drink?" Carbine invited.

Thus began a long friendship from a less than hopeful beginning.

For months Winchester was in a quandary over what to do with, or what to make of, this rural North Carolinian Marsh Williams. He was certainly not an eight-to-five employee. Sometimes he would stay at the plant for several consecutive days. At other times he would disapear for a few days and no one, including the management, knew where he was or what he was doing. Also, contrary to company rules, Marshall Williams did not consider himself fully dressed unless he had on his person at all times two .45 automatics, fully loaded. The familiar bulge under his coat was ever present, and both automatics were fully visible whenever the coat was removed.

Despite this nonconformity, Winchester finally and wisely realized it was much to its advantage to let this man go his own way. As a result of this wise decision things began to happen; for example, Williams invented an automatic .50 caliber rifle with box magazine.

"Only one of these rifles was ever built," Williams pointed out, "and Winchester loaned that rifle to Frankfurt Arsenal so they could further their experiments with the .50 caliber machine gun cartridge. They had no weapon to work with. Later the rifle was lost and was traced and found at Frankfurt Arsenal. As far as we know, it was returned to Winchester and is still a part of the Winchester collection. I wish to hell I had it. I'd a knowed where it was from the start!" he promised. (Williams received no royalty for this contribution to the development of the now-familiar .50 caliber cartridge and machine gun.)

"Another weapon I developed using my short-stroke piston," Carbine noted, "was the Winchester Automatic Rifle (WAR). Ten of these were built and proved to have

214

many advantages over the old Browning Automatic Rifle.
For instance, the bipod was much better and easier to put
into operation. Secondly, using my short-stroke piston, you
utilized the gas close to the breech of the weapon that was
so hot that it burned off the carbon that builds up on
weapons taking gas from the muzzle, and this gives them
trouble-free operation with no necessity of cleaning and
continually adjusting the gas piston. My automatic rifle
had many other advantages, including a reduction in
weight and much more streamlined lines for better handling. Due to the war, they did not have time to completely
retool and get this into production, so they continued to
produce and utilize what they already had. I sincerely feel
that this particular weapon is far superior in many ways
to many of the weapons in use today." (See photograph of
ten Winchester Automatic Rifles, Photo 39.)

"I changed my set-up with Winchester later on,"
Williams continued, "and worked as an independent,
which suited me much better. It was at that time that I
returned to my home near Godwin and it was from here
that I have worked ever since in my own little shop and
my own farm. Ross, I had good reason for this change.
During World War II it was plumb knockdown, drag-out
at Winchester. For instance, I had three names—for
security reasons. I was going by my own name, David
Marshall Williams, also as 'Mr. Davis,' and the third one
was according to where I was. Also, while it was flatly
denied by Winchester officials, there was one SOB first
class there at Winchester who was a professional gun idea
thief. He's dead now and I don't care."

Carbine readily acknowledged that this gun thievery
was not the doings of Winchester Arms Company. The
officials did not condone or really know the extent of what
was going on. But, as is often the case in industry, persons
working for their own benefit or for outsiders infiltrate a
company and steal ideas.

Carbine continued: "I was minding my own business
here in Godwin and John Olin's father, Mr. Frederick Olin,
insisted that I come to Winchester to get them out of a rut.

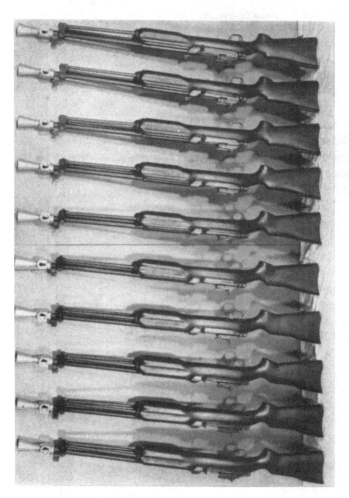

Photo 39. The WAR — Winchester Automatic Rifle. "I developed this for Winchester and, in my opinion, it had many features that were better than the old BAR (Browning Automatic Rifle), but the war came along and we never got this beauty into production. It would have been a winner", Carbine said.

John expressed the same thoughts. When I finally agreed and went, Mr. Frederick Olin, a most honorable gentleman if I've ever met any, rode me in my first Cadillac. They put me up in the biggest hotel in New Haven, the Hotel Taft, at Mr. Olin's own request, and saw to it that I had ample transportation with a company Cadillac. I worked with another man, an honorable gentleman named Ralph Clarkson. He was a plumb all right fellow. When it came to milling machines and precision tools, he didn't take a backseat to nobody.

"I quickly realized," Carbine continued, "that there was really a professional gun thievery going on at Winchester and it was well organized. A fellow would leave an experimental model on his workbench and go to eat and everyone would converge on his table to see what in the world he was making.

"They did not pull this trick on me. But one SOB did put his name on my patent," he claimed. "He was working for me as a tool and die maker — not the best, but he could turn out something pretty quick if you had to have it. I'll give him credit for that all right. O.K. He put his name on one of my patent applications and Winchester had its own patent department. When I found out about it, I plumb exploded. Everyone there knew I sported guns. As you know, I always do. Anyway, Edwin Pugsley was head of research and a Winchester vice-president at that time. He was a Yale graduate and a polished gentleman, an honorable man. He was known to look out for Winchester's interests. That's for damn sure! Pugsley thought I was going to shoot that SOB. I reckon it was Ralph Clarkson, bless him, who called Pugsley up and said, 'Come up quick! I think Marsh is going to kill _____ .' Man he had to come hell-for-breakfast to get there so quickly, for Winchester is a big place.

"He did all in his power to get us to make up, for hellfire, a war was on. I finally agreed. I said, 'I'll make up. I don't hate nobody.' I had a bell that I rang if I wanted certain people to come in. I rang that bell and _____ came in. We shook hands and he walked out. It was short and sweet. I had a desk — but who the hell sits at a desk? I sat down at the workbench that I had in there to cool off a little, and from the tool and lathe rooms, boys began to come in and start staring at me. We liked to joke one another so I said, 'What the hell are you looking at me like that for? What's the matter?'

"The spokesman said, 'We wanted to come in and see if you had your hands. Did he steal your hands?' We all had a good laugh. I later discussed this with my Washington lawyer and he said, 'Marsh, you are upset. As far as the money goes, will it make any difference?'

"I said, 'No.'

" 'Won't make a dime's bit of difference,' he said. 'Why don't you forget it then?'

"I did this," Carbine conceded, "and it was one of the big mistakes and the only bad advice my lawyer ever gave me. Ross, I tell you this just to give you an idea of how tough a game it was in the field of inventing and manufacturing weapons."

Gordon Williams was convinced that his brother's suspicions of professional gun thievery at Winchester were justified:

"Pugsley was so upset about Marsh's attitude toward those trying to steal his ideas, and so afraid Marsh would hurt someone," Gordon confided, "that he called me to come to New Haven as soon as possible. I took the next train, met with Marsh, was convinced that his fears were justified and told Pugsley this. Edwin Pugsley didn't like this but offered me a job with Winchester, hoping that I would calm Marsh down. I refused but I did remain in New Haven with Marsh for six months at my own expense, and I feel that my presence there kept the lid from blowing off. Marsh was hot about the goings-on at Winchester, and a certain few had every right to be afraid.

"There would have been serious trouble if he had found that someone was sabotaging his work or stealing his ideas," Gordon concluded.

Photo 1-37   General Douglas MacArthur autographs one of "Carbines" famed inventions, his M-1 Carbine (R.E. Beard).

CHAPTER 10
Fame, Kindness and Fleeting Cash

To Hollywood

I asked Carbine to tell me about going to Hollywood during the filming of the movie which depicted his life. I must admit that I was somewhat exasperated, but frankly, amused, when it turned out that Carbine was more interested in the experience of riding in the diesel engine with the engineer on the trip out — and remembered more details about this — than that of meeting with MGM to make the movie.

"Shortly after Captain Peoples wrote the article in *Reader's Digest* about me," Carbine began, "I received a call asking that I come to Hollywood. MGM's people suggested strongly that they wanted to do a movie about me. Hot dog! Off to Hollywood I went. I went on a train and, while rolling, I put on a gun show in the parlor car. Folks seemed to enjoy this.

"That night," he said, in beginning to tell of an incident that occurred along the way, "I was restless so I went forward to the engine and rode the rest of the way up there with the engineer. Now on the way out there the engineer said to me, 'I want to show you our girlfriend pretty soon.' Being a man that has seen a few things, I didn't say anything. I didn't get wise at all, I just listened and looked. 'Well now, we're coming pretty close and here she'll be pretty soon.' I began to look over there and I saw a young girl. I'd say she was around twelve or thirteen, but she might have been fifteen. She was not too far away from the railroad in a house on the ground floor and she was waving. Before we got there, the engineer was talking to her on the whistle.

"It so developed that this girl had been bothered with some kind of illness that she couldn't get out of bed," Carbine continued. "She couldn't do much of anything. And I guess her people weren't too able to do much about it. The railroad men heard of it and they put up the money and had her well taken care of, until they got her almost recovered, at least to the extent that she could get out of bed and wave at them. But formerly she would have to wave from the bed."

At length Carbine Williams reached his destination.

"On the diesel we went on into Hollywood. I never saw so many people trying to get ahead of the diesel to go to work that morning. It just goes to show you how people will do, trying to get to work and didn't want to wait for the train. And the diesel engineer—what time he wasn't reaching for the whistle cord, he was a blowing the whistle!

"We met with MGM in Hollywood and agreed to make the movie. I saw here a way to tell my son David (Photo 40) my story so that he would better understand me. I could not have handled it if David would have been ashamed of me. I returned several times to Hollywood before the making of the movie and I admit that I lived the part of the big spender and party fellow. I spent more than I made, but some parts of the trip were fun for sure," Carbine acknowledged.

"While there," he continued, "I met and got to know and admire Jimmy Stewart, a real fine man, and of course, Wendell Corey, Jean Hagen and the others who were to be in the movie. I carried several guns out there with me but they used only one, as you know. I enjoyed being behind the scenes and they asked for my advice and direction on many things. For instance, I spent considerable time show-

Photo 40. David Marshall Williams, Jr. and the inventor during the making of the movie, *Carbine Williams*. David, Jr., now a grown man, has returned to make his home near Godwin on the family farm.

ing Jimmy Stewart how to wear and walk in leg irons. It was fun for sure watching him the first few times, until I taught him to wear the leather throng over the calf of his leg to tuck the chains in for walking purposes.

"I had to build the still for them, too," he continued, "and there was lots of kidding about that. Lots of the fellows strongly suggested that I fire her up and run a batch or two for ol' times sake. I smiled and they knew my whiskey-making days were over. I showed them what guns to use in different scenes and often suggested changes in the script that made it more accurate."

In getting Carbine to tell me about the world premiere showing of his movie in Fayetteville, North Carolina, I had the distinct feeling that I was, in a way, seeing a kid telling about his first birthday party. Carbine was pleased to talk about this and you could easily tell that this was one of the happiest times of his life.

"REB, they had printed a beautiful program telling about the world premiere of my movie, and I was pleased when we arrived at the Colonial Theater to find that the soldiers at Fort Bragg had formed an honor guard of fine soldiers standing at attention with the M-1 carbine slung on their shoulders. I stopped and talked to several of these boys. There were lots of officials running around and things were friendly all the way round. It was something sitting there in that theater watching a big part of your life being shown back to you. Jimmy Stewart sho' did a fine job. He was a man's man in my book.

"I was pleased that they had the world premiere of my movie in Fayetteville," Carbine continued, "I was especially grateful for the warm reception that the folks there and abouts gave me and my family. The movie was shown Thursday night, April 24, 1952, following Carbine Williams Day celebrations. It was a great and memorable occasion," he reminisced.

"Following the initial showing of that movie, I was on a whirlwind ride. We had a big Cadillac and we appeared at theaters all over the country, day and night,

Photo 41. The real Williams family and its Hollywood counterpart. At left, actors Jimmy Stewart, who played Carbine; Bobby Hyatt, who played David Jr.; Jean Hagen, who played Miss Maggie. At right, David Marshall Williams, Miss Maggie Williams and David Marshall, Jr.

as fast as we could get there. This exciting time came to an end almost as quickly as it began.

"About the time of the movie, *Fawcett Movie Comic* books came out with a comic book, telling my story. I was No. 19 in October of 1952. They sure missed the boat in one picture. They showed me converting the .45 to a .22, but the picture showed me shooting a revolver rather than an automatic. It was a good story though."

Carbine did not remember a single important fact about the making of the movie *Carbine Williams*. A year after his death, however, David Jr., while going through a trunk, found a little black notebook containing a daily account of Marshall Williams' experiences while making the movie in Hollywood. The following is extracted from that diary:

December 10, 1951

MGM Studio—Shooting of MGM "Carbine Williams" began. James Stuart, Jean Hagen and many others (Photo 41) were shot in various scenes—including family scenes—all children and Ma and Pa meet Senator.

I was supervising the setting up of Whiskey still—it is very good. Had picture made with Senator and myself at still.

December 11, 1951

At MGM—James Stewart and Jean Hagen made scene in dining room & kitchen. Had pictures made with Stewart and myself at Whiskey still. AP photographer made them. Lionel Asher was with AP photographer.

December 13, 1951

MGM Studio—Scenes at still showing Stewart when scaulded by hot mash when he pulled cap from still.

December 14, 1951

MGM Studio—Raid on my still showing gun fight and so on—at still.

December 15, 1951
Friday—MGM Studio—On Lot No. 3 shooting scene on railroad section crew or gang. Scene in shop where stills are being made. I am introduced in shop. Night scenes in Godwin where I loved.

December 16, 1951
Saturday—MGM Studio— Studio Stage No. 15— Stewart and Jean Hagen walking through woods with dog and gun. Stewart shoots bird and while on walk proposes marriage to Jean. Stewart goes to old Fort— Jean finds him there. He does not know she is coming. He agrees to surrender to Sheriff. Jean writes me a letter while at Fort. She went there for memories and inspiration. She does a very wonderful job with great emotion and feeling—very effective on me at least.

December   , 1951
Friday—MGM—Scene working in the rain and going up steep hill. Also scene on train coming from Blue Ridge mountain camp near Robinsonville, N.C. This was Capt. Peoples camp & we are on the way to Caledonia. Stewart tears up letter he got from home.

January 2, 1952
MGM Studio—Scenes on Caledonia

January 3, 1952
MGM Studio—Scenes on Caledonia

January 4, 1952
MGM Studio—Scenes on Caledonia

January 5, 1952
MGM Studio—Scenes on Caledonia—Also I worked on movable chamber 35 cal. rifle for use in picture.

Tuesday—Picnic scene

Wednesday—Court scene which included hung jury.

Thursday—Court scene— I get a 30 year sentence— We have decided to compromise on 2nd degree sentence.

Friday—Stewart returning home to meet the family when he is on way to State Prison. The whole family is there. The scene is 30 miles from Hollywood in country at a nice farm house.

January 7, 1952

MGM Studio—Scenes in Capt. Peoples' office on Caledonia prison farm—also in Prison Board Office in Raleigh, N.C. in State Prison Commission Office, Raleigh, N.C. Saw James Stewart's Mother, Father and wife again today.

January 8, 1952

MGM Studio—Scenes at Winchester Arms Co & also in model room & Mr. Swanson's office. Sheriff Biscoluiz was over to see the shooting. Several news men were there and took many pictures with the Sheriff, myself Stewart & others. Also some with Director Richard Thorpe.

January 9, 1952

MGM Studio—Caledonia Prison Farm—This included Stewart shooting the .35 calibre movable chamber rifle—it worked good. Stewart's Father and Mother were there. He, Stewart's Father gave me an autographed picture of their house.

Later, Bobby Hyatt, playing David's part on Stage 15 when we—Stewart & he are driving over to State Prison at Raleigh. Also scenes of me leaving Caledonia State Prison Farm.

January 10, 1952

At MGM Studio—Scenes showing David on trip to Central Prison to talk with Capt. Peoples.

January 11, 1952

Tiny—myself— David & Leon at MGM Studio—Saw

Scenes showing Stewart & Bobby leaving Central
Prison after talk with Capt. Peoples.

January 12, 1952

Tiny—myself—David & Leon was at MGM Studio
& saw last shot in Carbine Williams.

January 13, 1952

Day of Rest—At Hollywood Knickerbocker Hotel.
Tiny, David, Leon and myself were there.

January 14, 1952

MGM Studio—I went over to have pictures made of
myself James Stewart & Jane Hagen for publicity.
Louis Calhern was there.

January 15, 1952

MGM Studios—Talked with Mr. Jordan on publicity.
Introduced by Mr. Rothwell of MGM. Visited Mr.
Saunders House. Tiny, David, Leon and myself.

January 16, 1952

Wednesday—Around Hollywood with Tiny, David
& Leon.

January 17, 1952

Thursday—Around Hollywood with Tiny, David and
Leon.

January 18, 1952

Friday—MGM Studio—In Mr. Deutrech's office &
decided to "retake" one scene. Saw considerable of
picture run & Deutrech & Thorpe were here with
many others. Later went to Deutrechs house & had
supper. Then went to Knickerbocker Hotel & joined
Tiny, David and Leon.

January 19, 1952

Around Los Angeles—Tiny, David, Leon & myself
went to visit Al Jennings, noted old West *outlaw*. Bob
Brown drove us over in his car.

January 20, 1952

Sunday—Around Hollywood—Tiny, David, Leon and myself.

January 21, 1952

Monday—Tiny, David, Leon left Los Angles on Sunset Limited—8 PM via New Orleans for Fayetteville—home. We were at MGM studio during morning.

January 22, 1952

Tuesday—Main Street L.A. to see about hats—holsters & knives.

January 31, 1952

Thursday—At MGM Studio—Talked about me going on a tour & publicity on "Carbine Williams". Had lunch with Chief Hendry and John Rothwell & Frank Whitbeck. Talked with Eddie Lawrence.

February 4, 1952

At MGM Studio—Had a test made of myself—*A Screen Test A Short Movie* to see how I would look and do on the screen. To be used in Advertising the "Carbine" Williams picture.

February 7, 1952

Thursday—At MGM Studio. Talked with Mr. Morta—Rothwell and others—also Frank Whitbeck. Saw Film run of me in my test. Everyone thought I was very good. It looked alright to me.

February 9, 1952

Saturday—Went to MGM—AM—Left Los Angles 12:30 PM—noon for N.Y. City on Santa Fe Super Chief Car PA 28—Drawing Room "D"

February 10, 1952

Sunday—Aboard Sante Fe Super Chief. Before we arrived Dodge City, Kan., Conductor Thompson wired General Manager Bucanan for permission to ride Diesel Engine. Permission was granted so—when train stopped at Dodge City a new engine crew came on and I rode engine No. 20.

February 13, 1952

Wednesday—A meeting was held in my room in hotel regarding publicity. Larry Smitz, Gene Casey, Bill Dipperman, Dan Terrell, Fay Ridenour was there.

February 18, 1952

Monday—Merrill Lindsay & myself went to Winchester & talked to Mr. Hartley & Mr. Schode about publicity. On my way to N.Y. City I stopped at Bridgeport to talk to O'Donnell. He made out my tax papers.

February 19, 1952

Tuesday—Jules Rosenthal called me. Asked me to call Harry Fox at 45 Rockefeller Plaza. I did and had a conference in his office 3:00 PM. Miss Sheelagh Dille introduced and in conference. These people were interested in a promotions deal.

February 26, 1952

Tuesday—Called MGM Studio—the preview— Sneak Preview of "Carbine" Williams was shown at Pickwood Theatre. Leon and myself was there. Things were very fine.

February 29, 1952

Friday—At MGM Studio and saw the making *Eagle in My Cap* showing about when the atom bomb was dropped on Japan. Robert Taylor—Eleanor Parker & Marlyn Erskine were stars. Had picture with Parker and Erskine.

March 1, 1952.

Saturday—At MGM—Leon and myself. We brought all my guns & things away that was in picture.

March 14, 1952

Friday—At MGM Studio with John Rothwell. Had dinner with about 12 MGM representatives from all over USA. Had pictures made at dinner table.

230

March 25, 1952

Tuesday — MGM Studio — Made radio program with Jim Stewart.

March 26, 1952

Wednesday — MGM Studio at a newsman's showing — Carbine Williams. The projection room was crowded with newspaper people and Magazine people.

March 30, 1952

Sunday — Went to William Bowes house. Myrna Loy owned the house. Williams Bowes bought it for her. He & his wife drove me home from Chateau Des Fleures at 6626 Franklin Avenue.

April 1, 1952

Tuesday — Talked with Al Jennings, old West Bank Robber & outlaw. I am to see him before I go home to North Carolina as I may never see him again.

April 2, 1952

Wednesday — Shell Shop — Six cases of carbine ammunition and to Bavlin Saddle Shop. Looked and felt of Gen. Custer's Saddle.

April 4, 1952

Friday — Left Hollywood and Los Angles at 12:30 PM on Sante Fe Super Chief for N.Y. City.

April 7, 1952

Monday — Arrived N.Y. City 9:30 AM. Went to see Life Magazine people. Called collect to Dan Terrell MGM office. Terrill said he would show the movie Carbine Williams 3:30 Tuesday 8th. I called Samuel F. Pryon Jr. and told him about it. He wants to see it. Gordon, Leon, myself, Ridenour, Dawkin & Moss & Myrover went to circus at Madison Square Garden.

Cash — His Trademark

Marshall Williams never had much money in his early life but he believed in having whatever was his in cold cash.

To him a bank check was nothing more than an IOU. This desire for cash continued to manifest itself when Winchester decided to settle with Williams for his having developed the now-famous .30 caliber M-1 carbine. Called into the office, Williams was offered a check in the amount of $234,001.46 by company officials. Williams not only refused the check, expressing his dislike for such tokens of money, but further shocked the arms officials by flatly stating, "I don't do no business on any damned Friday! It is bad luck." He walked out.

Flabbergasted, the officials implemented efforts to find out just exactly when Marshal Williams liked to do business and exactly how he proposed to be paid.

"All they had to do was come right out and ask," Carbine said, simplifying the matter. "I wanted to be paid in cash." On a day designated, an armored car arrived and Williams signed a receipt certifying that he had received, in cash, $234,001.46!

"It was just as simple as that," Williams explained. "Even with the big bills, it filled the pockets of my hunting coat and the game pouch in the rear, too. Winchester was plenty concerned that I was carrying that kind of cash but I wasn't concerned at all, for with it, as always, I was carrying my two .45 automatics; and, as you know, I knew how to use them.

"It was the most money I had ever seen in my life," Williams acknowledged, "and I headed for New York. I never was much for dressing up so I guess to those city folks I looked plumb country. I sure didn't talk like them. I went into one of them fancy Fifth Avenue jewelry stores and my eyes fell dead on an emerald-cut diamond ring about the size of a postage stamp, mounted in platinum. I asked a feller working there, 'How much is that there?' and pointed to the ring that had struck my eye. That feller kind of eyed me and very loftily said, with a smile, 'Sir, that ring is $44,000.' Ross, you should've seen the expression on that feller's face when I reached in my hunting jacket, pulled out a stack of bills and peeled off forty-four of them."

"Don't bother to wrap it," Williams retorted as he nonchalantly dropped the ring into his coat pocket.

"Ross, some damned body is still enjoying that ring for I got drunk in New York and lost the damned thing! I still have the receipt for it, and that feller's expression was plumb worth the price."

Not one who believed in putting his cash into stocks and bonds, Williams invested in a number of businesses, including a hotel, restaurant, lounge, razor blade factory and vitamin plant, always leaving the running of the businesses to partners. He had fairly good beginner's luck, but most of these businesses sooner or later absorbed his cash or he would shed his acquisitions.

It is a well-known fact that Williams was an easy mark when someone came to him asking him for help. Many thousands of dollars were handed to "friends in need," then and there, when the need was expressed. Few of these friends were around when Williams' money ran out. Possibly this was all right too, for Williams was a proud man, not on known to ask for help.

Once while I was shooting with Carbine, he was drawing a bull's eye on a piece of paper. He started smiling and flipped the paper over. It was an order blank for Williams Vitamins. "They didn't make me any money, Ross," he said with a smile, "but they were damned good vitamins. I took them myself." Rummaging around under the workbench, he dug out a bottle of Williams Vitamins and an order blank tablet. Pressing these items into my hand, he laughed and said, "Try these, Ross. If I ever go back in the business, you will have order blanks to order from me. If not, these forms made damned good targets."

A more serious expression came to Marshall Williams' face and he said, quietly, "It was fun while it lasted. I cut a plumb wide path there for awhile."

Continuing talking about the days when he was in the money, Marshall Williams laughed again and said, "I had worn work clothes and bib overalls most of my life and I decided to buy some real store-bought duds. The salesman began showing me some expensive suits and stressed how nice I looked in stripes. I never cracked a smile and I said, 'Say, were you in prison the same time I was?' He nearly dropped dead for, of course, he knew I had been in prison but had not thought about that when he mentioned that I looked good in stripes.

"I followed through by saying, 'Yeah, I do look pretty good in stripes, but if you don't mind, I want these small and running up and down—not around and around.' Before I started laughing, that salesman was so damned nervous and upset he could not properly measure me or even fill out the order blank. I got many a good laugh out of that."

The Forgotten Man

On being pardoned, a former prisoner, one might anticipate, would try to forget all association with prison and would have no desire to revisit such facilities. Such was not the case with Marshall Williams. As fame and honor came his way, he felt compelled to return there. He wanted to see again the cell in which he had been initially confined, and he wanted to see again the guards and prisoners he had known.

Did prison visits offer a grim reminder as to how fortunate he was to be free? This we will never know, but we do know these things. This loner, this usually rather shy but tough man, found that he had made something of his life—that society had forgiven if not forgotten—that it had allowed him the chance to make his life worthwhile. He felt that all men should have this opportunity. Again and again he addressed groups of prisoners, stressing that they, too, would have a chance on the outside if they worked toward that end. In addition, quietly and without fanfare, Williams handed out dollar after dollar from his pocket to wives, sons and daughters of those confined in prison.

One particular example of his concern for his fellow man involved a Negro man confined to prison for life. Carbine referred to him as the "forgotten man."

"Ross, he was what you call a nobody—forgotten there," Carbine reflected. "He had no family and no one on the outside to say or do anything for him. No one tried to get him out nor did anyone even know that he was in there — or give a damn, for that matter. Probably he would have never gotten out. On a visit to prison to make a talk, I met him and he remembered me. We talked man to man. I made some contacts and no clear record of his crimes could even be found. I was very fortunate in being instrumental in getting this man a pardon and he lived a good life thereafter."

"Why did you do this?" I asked Carbine.

"He was a man. He was a good man, and there was just no need to keep him in a cage."

The tough can be gentle and such was the case with Marshall Williams. No man was too small or insignificant to reach Williams' heart if he approached him man-to-man in an honest, truthful manner.

Carbine Williams Day

It is indeed a rare occasion when an ex-convict, a man who has served time for murder, returns to his home town to be honored by national, state and local officials for his international accomplishments. But such was the case with Carbine Williams.

Williams returned to Fayetteville, North Carolina, for Carbine Williams Day on April 24, 1952, an event which included the premiere of the film concerning his life. The following is a transcript of an actual recording of events of that day. The emcee was Glenn Cobb, a local attorney.

"The ceremonies began in the ballroom of the Prince Charles Hotel. As newsmen from all over the world stood by, Carbine Williams and Wendell Corey arrived in a Cadillac convertible and a chauffeur opened the doors. As he did, the dignitaries began to walk toward the hotel. Accompanying Carbine, in his own car, was Fayetteville's most famous historian, John A. Oates.

"Carbine Williams has stepped to the ground. The chauffeurs are opening the other doors in the procession of automobiles. Passing in front of our stands here is the colorful Fayetteville High School Band. Approaching the steps is Carbine Williams; Mrs. Williams; David Jr., the son of Carbine Williams; Robert Belton, head of the Exchange Club; Wendell Corey and others too numerous to mention. . . .Carbine waves a warm greeting to the high sheriff and steps up to give him a warm handshake to greet him. The friendliness between these two men is part of the. . .reason for this occasion today.

"Now let's go straight away and pick up the presentation ceremonies here on the courthouse steps. Ladies and gentlemen, at this time the United States Army Band will play." [Band plays.]

Dr. Samuel High of Holland Presbyterian Church in Fayetteville gave the invocation:

"Our Father, we thank Thee for this country of which we are a part. We thank Thee that it is a country ruled by laws and not by the dictates of dictators. We pray Thee that You will give to this community Thy blessings. Let us as individual citizens be the sort of people who will make this a better place in which to live because we have been here. Especially do we thank Thee for this man whom we honor this day and for the long years in which he served on the side of law and right. We pray for Thy blessing upon him throughout all of the years of his life and for all those who shall seek in this community to uphold the law and for all those who are on the side of right. May this be a community in which men and women can bind themselves together for the highest welfare and good of all concerned. Bless us as we submit ourselves to Thee and as together we seek to learn how to live in a world which Thou can approve. Amen."

The emcee continued with the day's activities: "We could have looked far and wide and throughout the length and breadth of the United States, but I do not believe that we could have found a man who is more appropriate to give or to present this portrait [of Sheriff N.H. McGeachy] today. At this time I desire to present to you Fayetteville's own historian, a man who needs no introduction in North

Carolina or in the southeastern section of the United States: the Honorable John A. Oates."

Oates made a presentation preceding the unveiling of McGeacy's portrait which Marshall Williams presented to Cumberland County:

"Mr. Williams, Sheriff McGeachy and your families, and ladies and gentlemen. This is the greatest crowd of people that has gathered together in Fayetteville since Sherman was here in 1865. We had a great celebration here in 1889 and another one in 1939, but this group of people that line the streets of the City of Fayetteville is larger in number and in appreciation than either one of those two events.

"When General MacArthur was forced to leave the Philippine Islands he said, 'I will come back. I will come back.' On November 21, 1921, David Marshall Williams had to leave Cumberland County but he said in his own soul then, 'I will come back,' and today he's here being honored by the assembled thousands of the southeastern part of North Carolina. The great day, however, was not the day that we celebrate, but it was the day that he left here because of a combination of circumstances. Mr. Williams suffered some punishment, but through the courtesy and confidence of Sheriff McGeachy, the spirit and the soul of David Marshall Williams did not die. The flame kept on burning, even though he was confined where he couldn't get out. The spirit kept burning. He became the greatest inventor of firearms in the history of our country. I wish for Sheriff McGeachy to stand. [Applause] It was his courtesy to David Marshall Williams and his confidence in him that made him determined that he would make a success of himself after he got out of prison.

"When they left the old courthouse on that fateful day going to Raleigh, Sheriff McGeachy took him with him as he would any other passenger and not as a prisoner. He gave him the glad hand and not handcuffs, and when he got to his home between here and Dunn he said, 'Marshall, get out and go yonder in the house and tell your folks goodbye. I'll stay here in the car.' Marshall Williams said in his soul, 'That sort of thing must be repaid by me. I can't afford to go back on it.' He went in the house and talked to his people. He told them that he was going away on a visit, but will come back, as Sheriff McGeachy waited for him there in the car. When he got back, he was ready for him to take him away.

"I ask the men who have those guns to hold them up, please — from the Army. Hold up your guns. That gun carries in it the personality and the life of David Marshall Williams. When he was shut up and couldn't get out, he took such tools that he could get together in the prison camp and he worked on the making of that gun. And it is that gun that our boys in Korea are carrying today. It's that gun that it looks like will be used in the defense of Europe because Williams' gun is the greatest gun in the world today for the defense of the Stars and Stripes.

"Mr. Williams wanted to repay Sheriff McGeachy. All that he could do was not in money, but [he] was to leave something in the courthouse here so that succeeding generations could see an expression of his appreciation. This is the first time in riding down the street that I had the honor of a ride with a millionaire. And he made it on that gun.

"He's kin to me [but] he won't own it. We both came from Sampson County and I was born about two miles from where his mother and grandmother came from. I am glad that it is my privilege to present this portrait. I am honored by it. I do no honor to the occasion.

"Sheriff McGeachy is a Cumberland County man on his mother's side. She was a McNeil that lived on the south bank of Rock Fish Creek as you go toward Lumberton. You know who the McNeils are.

"The story is told that there was a good old woman in the first row of the church. This good old woman dipped snuff. She would sit right in front of the pulpit so she could hear good while the preacher was preaching. She got right next to a crack in the floor so she could spit through it when the occasion demanded it. The preacher was preaching on Jesus. He said, 'Who was the mother of Jesus?' This old lady thought he needed an answer. She was partially deaf. She said, 'Parson,' (with a little bit of juice in her mouth) 'Parson, I'm not certain myself but I always heard that the mother of Jesus was a McNeil.'

"Sheriff McGreachy is a descendant of the McNeils. His grandfather was sheriff of Cumberland County thirty-odd years and gave it up. He said he wanted somebody else to have a chance at it. Sheriff McGreachy served this county for thirty years. Half of his life was spent in the courthouse. And I have never yet heard him charged of being unkind or cruel to a prisoner under his care.

"What else? He's a great Presbyterian. . . .He's a military man. He was a major in the North Carolina Guards. He served in the Spanish-American War. And I thought the handsomest man that I have ever seen. Sheriff McGeachy, when he came back from that war marching down the streets of Fayetteville, the woman all wanted him.

"They just told me to speak five minutes, but not to exceed eight. Well, I am putting the same regulations on you that they put on food and other things in these days, a minimum and a maximum.

"But, anyway, one final word about the Sheriff. He loved the courthouse. It was over there where you see that tower that he first came in office. Then he came here. It had been moved from over next to where I live; that was Courthouse Square at that time. When they built that courthouse, it cost just a few thousand dollars. When they built this one, it cost three or four times as many.

"When they build the first one on Courthouse Square, there were two Scotsmen, the sheriff and an Italian who constituted the Board of Commissioners. One of the Scots-men had a sawmill, the other one had a brick mill. They had a great argument as to whether they should build a courthouse of brick or wood, so they could get a bite of it. The Italian was a tanner. He said, 'Boys, here's a way to settle this difficulty. Each of you wants the job. I suggest that we build the first story of it of brick, the second story of wood and that we cover it with leather.'

Photo 42. After being granted full pardon and following the world premiere of the movie, *Carbine Williams*, the inventor shakes hands with Sheriff N.H. McGeachy during a ceremony in which Williams presented to Cumberland County, N.C., a portrait of the sheriff.

"That was the start, the people that Sheriff McGeachy belonged to. I am a Scotsman myself and this is the definition of a Scotsman: He keeps everything he's got and he'll get what you've got if you don't watch him.

"Ladies and gentlemen. It is my privilege to present to you David Williams [Jr.], the son of David Marshall Williams, who is going to unveil this portrait which his father has given to the people of Cumberland County because of his appreciation of what Sheriff McGeachy did for him. (Photo 42) [Applause] We know of no one who could accept this portrait better than the own son of Sheriff McGeachy, Hector McGeachy, Jr."

Hector McGeachy, Jr. made an acceptance speech:

"I would like to express our most sincere appreciation to Marshall Williams and to those who have worked with him in presenting this very fine and most life-like portrait of Sheriff N. H. McGeachy. Without saying more in accepting this on behalf of Cumberland County and my father, Sheriff McGeachy, I would like to say that we not only appreciate the portrait but that we also very deeply appreciate the thought and the sentiment which goes with this portrait. Thank you."

The emcee then announced the conclusion of the events of the special day of recognition: "This concludes the presentation exercises, but it is only fitting to recognize at this time Marshall Williams, Mrs. Williams, his wife, Mr. Wendell Corey and Mr. Don Gibson, both of Hollywood. They will be at the theater at 7:30 tonight."

The ceremony was concluded with a benediction by a Dr. Howard, followed by the playing of "The Star Spangled Banner."

In the evening the world premiere of the movie *Carbine Williams* took place in Fayetteville's Colonial Theater.

Radio Interviews with Carbine Williams

A number of individuals and radio stations conducted interviews with Carbine Williams, but only a few seemed to be interested in telling the honest facts about this inventor. Among the exceptional interviews was that by radio station WPTF in Raleigh in 1952. I quickly add that I am pleased that it was another "Beard" who took this interest in Carbine. The transcript follows:

AN INTERVIEW WITH CARBINE WILLIAMS
Radio Station WPTF, Raleigh, N. C.

"Good evening, ladies and gentlemen. This is Sam Beard with a transcribed story which I feel will prove interesting and informative to all of us. It might be called the story of the Army's No. 1 rifle. We like to think of it as a success story of a fellow North Carolinian.

"At any rate it's the story of a country boy who was raised in a good Christian home, who wandered by the wayside, who at one time in his life was cast into the hands of the law to be tried for his life in North Carolina courts and served a long sentence in prison, yet a man who has had the fortitude to look adversity into the face, and who with the help of an understanding overseer was transformed from a so-called 'toughy' into a model 'A' prisoner, and later into an outstanding success to be recognized as America's No. 1 designer of guns. We are happy to have in the studios with us Mr. David Marshall Williams, who I believe is a fellow North Carolinian. Where were you born, Marsh?"

"I was born near Godwin, North Carolina, up about two miles in the country on a farm."

"You've been interested in guns all your life, I believe. Is that right?"

"That's right."

"Where did you develop your first one?"

"Well, I was about ten years old when I made my first gun. It was a wooden gun, made entirely of wood, and it had a reed barrel—a reinforced reed barrel."

"How did you manage to fire a gun made out of a reed?"

"Well, to keep the barrel from bursting, I wrapped it with strong fishing line."

"It was a muzzle-loading gun, I suppose. What did you use, black powder?"

"Yes, I used black powder and loaded it with one buck shot and sometimes I used small bird shot."

"How did you fire that gun?"

"I fired it with a match head, an old-fashioned match head. I'd cut it off and place it on the touch hole which is on the joint of the reed, and it in turn was fired by a wooden hammer which had a nail affixed."

"Well then, later on you developed other guns with steel and brass barrels, I suppose."

"Yes, that's right."

"Well, we'd like to touch very briefly on the tragedy of your life. Will you tell us very briefly what happened on the day of July 22, 1921?"

"Oh yes, on that date I was running a blockade whiskey still and it was raided by Sheriff McGeachy. They came in shooting and quite a number of shots were fired at the time and a deputy sheriff was killed."

"And you were to blame for that according to the law. Is that right?"

"Yes, that's right. The still belonged to me and they assumed that I was responsible."

"I see. You served quite a prison sentence for that, I believe."

"Oh yes, ten Christmases, about."

"Well, how did you finally gain your freedom?"

"Well, I was pardoned by Governor McLean."

"Well, that was in 1929, wasn't it?"

"That's right."

"All right. And during the time you were in prison, I believe you were stationed at the Caledonia Prison Farm."

"Yes, I was there."

"And did you carry on your work, your interest in guns, there?"

"Yes. After being there two or three years, I was placed in charge of the blacksmith shop and that gave me a good opportunity to pursue my work."

"Did you develop any particular type of gun while you were at Caledonia?"

"Oh yes, when the time came to begin this work, I went to Captain Peoples and explained it to him and I was surprised at him agreeing to it, but he did. And I developed the movable chamber principle there, the first gun, and I used it in a .22 caliber automatic rifle."

"Well, there is one thing that I would like to bring up right now, Marsh, if I may, and that is the story of your life is told. . .in the current issue of the *Reader's Digest* under the title of, 'The Most Unforgettable Character I've Met,' by Captain H. T. Peoples, the former superintendent of Caledonia State Prison Camp right here in North Carolina. Well, after you were pardoned, then did you go on with your gun work further?"

"Oh yes. Immediately after my pardon I made a machine shop out on the farm here at Godwin and continued my experimental work and made several guns."

"I see. I suppose you most famous invention of all is the Army carbine, isn't it?"

"Yes, that's right."

"Is that the one invention you're proudest of?"

"Yes, that's right."

"Well, I think you well might be, because every G.I. who's ever carried a carbine knows that it's a real life saver. Where did you get the idea for the carbine?"

"Well, the principal feature of the carbine is what I call the short-stroke principle and I developed the first model on Caledonia Prison Farm."

"It has some other qualities, too, some other advantages that make it particularly well suited for Army and Marine use."

"Oh yes, this short-stroke piston is not subject to being fouled by elements of combustion, it doesn't require any cleaning and it takes its power from the high-pressure zone in the barrel. Therefore, it gives a great amount of operating energy, which is necessary to operate a rifle under adverse military conditions."

"We would like to also mention in passing that in the current issue of *Collier's Magazine* the story of Carbine Williams is told, and in that article, which we've just finished, General Mark Clark, chief of the Army Field Forces, is quoted, saying, 'It was a significant development in small arms.' Who made that gun, by the way?"

"Well, Winchester Repeating Arms was one of the manufacturers, General Motors, Underwood-Elliot typewriter people and about a dozen, all told. They made about eight million."

"Eight million during World War II?"

"That's right."

"Are they still in use, by the way?"

"Oh yes, they're used all over the world by the Allied Forces."

"Our forces are using them now in Korea?"

"That's right. The United Nations Forces use them everywhere they operate."

"By the way, how many patents, other than the carbine, do you have to your credit?"

"Oh, about sixty."

"About sixty patents. Are you working on a royalty basis to companies using your patents, and do they pay you royalties for the use of them?"

"Oh yes, that's right. For instance, Remington Arms Company is making what they call the Model 550 Auto-Loading Rifle, .22 caliber. I get a royalty on these guns."

"Now is this .22 rifle that you developed at Caledonia the .22 automatic field rifle still in use by the Army, by the way?"

"The .22 rifle? Yes."

"Is it still in use, the one you developed, the first one you used, the one with the movable chamber?"

"That's right. The movable chamber was the principle upon which the .22 caliber machine gun was designed and the Colt Service Ace Pistol. These guns are used for training."

"All right, and there's one other very interesting thing that we'd like to mention for those people who are sportsmen or who are interested in guns and who read through magazines. In the current issue of *True Magazine*, again told from a different angle, the story of David Marshall Williams. I believe that's more or less on the technical angle, the story in *True*, isn't it?"

"Yes, that's right."

"We have that book and we see several diagrams and it is certainly a very interesting article to any of our listeners who are interested in the technical end of guns. Well, do you still maintain a shop and still interested in working on guns?"

"Oh yes, I work in the same shop down there in Godwin."

"You're still working and still developing new ideas. How many new ideas do you estimate that you have right now that you haven't been able to put into practice?"

"Well, I have a great many. It would take me about ten years to develop what I have in mind at the present time."

"You are going to be a very, very busy person in the future developing these things."

"Yes, I've always tried to keep busy."

"I would like to ask you this question. You are recognized to be America's foremost gun designer. Our forces are meeting the Communists in Korea, meeting the North Koreans as well as the Chinese. How do you feel about the way we stand up in the face of this opposition as far as our weapons are concerned?"

"Well, the American armies are far superior to any other army in the world and I believe we'll go on developing [weapons] by the various inventors and the various companies."

"We have the manpower, the brain power and also the manufacturing technique necessary to put these things into real production, don't we?"

"Yes, that's right."

"I wonder how many shells have been made for your Army carbine?"

"Well, it would be hard to estimate."

"I imagine so. Well, we certainly have enjoyed talking with you, David Marshall Williams, better known as 'Marsh,' a resident of North Carolina, a man who served a prison sentence (convicted of second-degree murder) and yet a man who did not use his adversities to just settle down to nothing, but a man who went on to amazing success in the field of the development of legal weapons and guns, not to be used in killing peaceful people here at home, but a man who has done a great deal of work in the development of weapons to be used in the defense of our country. Mr. Williams, all of North Carolina is proud of you for your success and we all wish you well."

Another good interview with Carbine was conducted by radio station WFLB of Fayetteville:

AN INTERVIEW WITH CARBINE WILLIAMS
Radio Station WFLB, Fayetteville, N. C.

"This is the story of a fellow North Carolinian who overcame great obstacles to obtain success as one of the nation's outstanding designers and inventors of guns. We are speaking of David Marshall Williams, a man who finished only seven [actually eight] years of formal schooling and at the age of fifteen and a half joined the Navy, passing for a man of seventeen. 'Marsh' Williams soon tired of the rolling oceans and returned home to try his hand at a Virginia military institute. For a man who loved the great outdoors and the freedom of the woods, life at the military institute soon became a dull routine, and he soon returned to his home at Godwin and was wed to his childhood sweetheart.

"In search of some means of support, Marsh Williams went to work for the Atlantic Coast Line Railroad as a section hand for $1.40 per day. This was hardly enough for a good living; he soon left the railroad and set up several blockade stills. For some time things were peaceful and the money was rolling in, but soon things began to change. During a raid on one of his stills a deputy sheriff was killed. Although it was never definitely determined who actually did the shooting, Marsh was owner of the still, was held responsible and sentenced to thirty years in prison. While serving approximately ten years [not quite eight] of this sentence, he launched himself on a career that has since brought him fame and fortune.

"This afternoon WFLB has taken this tape recorder to Marsh Williams' own workshop on the great plantation just out of Godwin, North Carolina. And right now standing before us is Marsh, who is right here in his workshop.

"First a few descriptive words of the shop. It has a large lathe over here. What kind of a lathe is that, Marsh?"

"That's a soft-spin lathe."

"Tell me, in actually making the guns, what do you actually use the lathe for?"

"For cleaning any round parts or boring or whenever you want to make a rifle barrel or something like that—anything that is round."

"Do you actually use it for boring the barrel? The way I understand it—I'm a layman at this, Marsh, you'll have to keep me straight on it—the actual boring of a rifle is very tedious, isn't it?"

"Oh yes, the making of a rifle barrel is a very precise job."

"And you use that lathe. I noticed that you have several others. That's just a simple grinder over there, isn't it?"

"Yes, that's right."

"This big machine here?"

"This machine is a Brown and Sharpe Universal miller. It will do any kind of milling. As a matter of fact, you can make any kind of gun part on it that you can conceive."

"In other words, lots of your own ideas have been worked out on that machine there."

"Oh yes, these tools here are tools that I have had ever since 1931 and on these machines I have made quite a few different guns."

"Around on the walls we see one large gun rack over there. Briefly, what kinds of rifles, shotguns, machine guns and everything else are hanging on the walls over there? Marshall, will you describe some of those guns for us?"

"The guns in the rack over there are the Browning Automatic Rifle, the Winchester 401, the carbine, the .30-'06 Springfield, the Browning Automatic Shotgun, Krag rifles, one experimental rifle, one model 1897 shotgun, one Maxim machine gun (aircraft model) and one Vickers machine gun (aircraft model)."

"In other words, there are guns all over the place. Over on the walls here there seems to be — if you've ever been to a dentist's office — one of these whirligigs that does all the boring. You have all of this machinery here well cleaned up and I might say the shop is immaculately clean. It's really a surprise. He has all sorts of punches and drills. What do you use those things for, Marsh?"

"Well now, all the punches you see here on the wall are actually some punches I made on Caledonia Farm while I was making time."

"In other words, you made your tools and then with your tools you made your guns."

"That's right."

"Well, Marsh, before we turn around here to this table that's loaded with guns — you have several rifles and guns that are forerunners to the carbine and all that — I wanted to ask you a few questions, Marsh, about your early life and the things that led to you finally becoming interested in guns, and a designer and inventor of guns. Marsh, during your early life, I think I've read in a manuscript here that's been printed all over the country, you actually made guns out of bamboo poles or reed?"

"Yes, I made pistols using reed for the barrel. The barrel was wrapped with strong fishing line so it wouldn't break when you use a pretty good charge of black powder."

"How old were you, Marsh, when you were making those guns?"

"I was about ten years old, I think."

"When I was ten, Marsh, I couldn't think of anything more to play with than blocks, or something like that. You were making your own guns at that age and, tell me, did they shoot with any accuracy at all?"

"Oh yes, you load them with bird shot and you could kill sparrows with them and if you use one buckshot it would penetrate a three-quarter-inch board. It's supposed to be a fatal wound."

"Is that right? Well, they were a pretty powerful gun. Did you ever have any to blow up on you?"

"Well, I had a good many to blow up on me from over-charges. Finally, I made a very small wooden pistol, and when I let the hammer down, it [the pistol], was so small the barrel was resting in the palm of my hand. The hammer slipped out from under my thumb, [ignited the matchhead] and fired off accidently. It gave me quite a wound in the palm of my hand."

"Well, Marsh, one thing I'd like to bring in right here. Would you advise any young boys today to try to make guns like that or actually experiment with guns at the age of ten or maybe nine?"

"I tell you not. It's a pretty dangerous proposition. I think somebody must have been watching over me during all that time. Otherwise, I probably would have lost an eye or something like that."

"Have you ever had a very serious accident?"

"No, none whatever."

"I think you were very lucky. I know that young boys shouldn't fool with guns that way, but Providence has guided you well and done a wonderful job, I think. Well, you said that you never had one of those small guns to blow up. I believe you did have an accident once, but that was through your own carelessness."

"Oh yes, pure carelessness, that's all."

"Another bit of good advice! Now I'm talking to a man who knows guns, and I have noticed in all the handling of these guns that he's done before we got our program started here, he is very careful with them. Marsh, do you think you can be too careful with a gun."

"No, you can't be too careful. The way to be careful is to observe the set rules, safety rules. If you do that you will never have an accident."

"One good thing is to really know your guns."

"That's right."

"On the way over here this afternoon, I was talking to Marsh and he told me that his actual education, as you know from the introduction, his formal education stopped at the seventh [eighth] grade, or through the seventh grade in school. I asked Marsh how he actually figured the pressure that's on these guns and the pressure built up in chambers and all that, and he told me that actually by mathematics, he didn't. In other words, Marsh Williams has some understanding of guns that he just knows. Like the young fellow told the teacher one time when she asked him a question that he couldn't answer, he said, 'I thought teachers just always know.' But Marsh, you seem to have a wonderful understanding of guns. You've taken all of these guns apart here and put 'em all back together this afternoon. Marsh, I'd like to ask you a few more questions about school life. How was your school life? Did you like school or didn't you like school or what?"

"Well, I didn't like school very much. I put up with it and I think I left school when I finished about the seventh grade, or a little better. No, I didn't like school. In going to school I would carry some of those wooden pistols I'd make and I used to get into quite a bit of trouble with the boys going down to the woods during recess to shoot them."

"I suppose you posed quite a problem for the teachers at that time, didn't you?"

"Oh, yes. I gave the teachers quite a run for their money."

"Now, in the Navy, Marsh. Did you learn anything about guns while you were in the Navy?"

"No, I don't think I learned anything about guns in the Navy that I didn't know before."

"In other words, you probably could have taught the Navy a little something."

"I think so. Yes."

"In later years you certainly showed the Army and the Ordnance Department quite a bit about guns. I know they really appreciated it. Marsh, getting along later in life, when you actually left the railroad and set up your stills around the country, you were doing this, to coin a phrase, to turn a fast buck. Is that right?"

"That's right."

"During that raid on the still that day when the deputy sheriff was killed, you don't have any actual knowledge as to who actually fired the shot, do you?"

"No, I really don't know who killed the sheriff. No. I never have admitted it; nobody's ever proved it. As a matter of fact, I don't think I did it."

"But the responsibility [rested with you in] that the still actually belonged to you, and you had to bear the brunt of the whole situation."

"That's right."

"Well Marsh, what we especially want to get around to here is this display of guns that we have. We have gone through quite a bit of your life. Now, actually what I want to cover right now is the period of Caledonia Prison Camp, while you were there under Captain Peoples. He was evidently a great man."

"Oh yes, he was a very fine fellow."

"He was rather lenient with you in letting you experiment with your guns."

"Oh yes. He went way out on a limb in doing that. Now he could have got himself fired for that. If something would have happened, of course they would have fired him and they might have even given him time for it."

"Well then, I'll say that it's a good thing for the world today that he did go out on that limb."

"I think so."

"Marsh, I notice that you have here on the table before us two actual rifles that you made while you were at Caledonia Prison Camp. I understand, as I told them before, you had to make your tools and then make your guns. Is that right?"

"That's right."

"Now, look now, Marsh, I'm gonna turn this over to you. Can you explain to the people listening these three guns?"

"This first rifle utilizes my floating chamber, which only moves to the rear about a fifteenth of an inch as this high-powered cartridge is fired. The movable chamber operates under maximum pressure, which is around fifty thousand pounds per square inch. This short rearward thrust of about a sixteenth of an inch under this pressure gives sufficient energy to the breech mechanism to open the gun, and the action, in turn, is closed by the closing spring."

"Marsh, was that the first gun you made?"

"Yes, that's right."

"Now, actually, was this movable chamber something that originated with you? In other words, that wasn't an improvement; you actually had the idea and created it yourself."

"Yes, that's right. It was not an improvement, it was a new principle in firearms."

"And a great one, the way it's used all over the world today. Well, Marsh, can we get along here to this next gun?"

"Yes, the second rifle here is a .22 Automatic Target Rifle. This .22 Automatic Target Rifle also makes use of the movable chamber principle, and from this movable chamber principle in caliber .22, the U.S. Machine Gun was developed and the Colt Service Ace Pistol. The .22 machine gun was a well set gun and was widely used for training purposes."

"Marsh, that .22 machine gun you speak of, that's the one you developed. You were commissioned by the Ordnance Department of the Army to develop that gun."

"Yes, that's right. General Hatcher issued the contract."

"I understand that it took you just approximately six weeks to design it and make a working model of it."

"Yes, that's right."

"Good, that's really great. Well, let's get on here to this next one. I think our time is running short, Marsh."

"Well, the other one is a different type of gun. It has a barrel that moves forward when it fires."

"The barrel moves forward and this doesn't have the movable chamber, in other words."

"No, that don't have the movable chamber."

"I see. You have one other rifle here and I think it's a Remington, isn't it?"

"Yes, this is a Remington Model 550 automatic. It uses the short, long and long rifle ammunition. What makes it operate with all of these cartridges is the fact that it uses the movable chamber principle, which increases the operating energy of the .22 short cartridge."

"In other words, this Remington is the direct outgrowth of the rifle you made in Caledonia Prison?"

"That's right."

"O.K. Right now we have a couple of demonstrations here Marsh is going to go through with us. First off we have a .45 Colt. Now how do you say it?"

"It's a .45 Colt automatic, which is the Army standard pistol."

"Well, Marsh is gonna shoot it a couple of times as a .45, then convert it to a .22 and shoot it real quick that way. So he's putting his clip into it and he's going to fire it right now [fired five shots]. There, you heard that and quite loud it was. I hope we're still on the air. Now he's going to convert that very quickly and we'll listen to him as he goes through it. He'll explain what he is doing with it."

"Well, in order to convert this from a .45 automatic to a .22, you remove the slide of the .45 automatic and the barrel and replace this slide with the Colt conversion unit caliber .22. And of course you use a .22 caliber magazine."

"And now he's got that all completed. Just that quick he converted it from a .45 to a .22. And here's the .22 [fired nine shots]. And it really shoots, believe me. From .45 to .22 in just that quick, in just a matter of seconds. Right now, Marsh, I noticed that you have that machine gun you developed in just six weeks set up over there. Is that the working model you made here in your shop?"

"Yes, I made this model right here."

"I wonder if you could fire that for us a few times just to give the audience listening an idea of just how rapidly it will fire — the .22 machine gun. Yes, he's running over here to get that machine gun now. Now our time is very short. He's got a belt. How many bullets are on that belt, Marsh?"

"A hundred bullets."

"I think he is going to fire just about all of them. We'll listen because this one really does shoot the bullets [fires one hundred rounds in three seconds]. That's all of them. One hundred just that quick, just that fast. Now probably the most famous of all Marsh's work is the Army carbine, which he is going to fire right now. First Marsh is gonna fire it semiautomatic and here is the way is goes [fires seventeen rounds]. It really puts them out. I think he's got another clip he wants to shoot there [fires twenty rounds]. I think he's driving me out that way. Here comes one more clip [fires twenty more rounds]. And there we have it. That was Marsh Williams firing his own guns, guns that he has created, guns that he has made to save lives, not to take lives. And as we read in the paper, it's a wonderful thing this little rifle, this carbine, is saving lives. Well, Marsh, we'd like to thank you very much for letting us bother you this afternoon here in your workshop. And we'd like to come out again sometime and see just what develops. Before we go we'd like to find out if you are working on anything new or important right now?"

"Yes, I'm always working on something new — a new aircraft machine gun and other material I couldn't mention."

"It's a shame you can't mention it now, but you are working on a new aircraft machine gun and other things. Well, good. Well Marsh, we appreciate you being so cooperative and helping us out this afternoon and we'd like to hear from you from time to time."

"Oh yes, I'd be glad for you to come out any time."

"I'd like to give you a plug right here right now. I forgot all about it until just a moment ago. Marsh is being featured next Friday night on the *We the People* television program in New York. Is that right?"

"It's Friday night."

"Oh, and by the way, Marsh was commissioned as special deputy here in Cumberland County by Sheriff Guy at the courthouse this morning. Is that where it took place?"

"Yes, that's right."

"Marsh, I understand that you have quite a few cards, or are deputy sheriff all over the country, in quite a few places. Could you name them right quick for us?"

"Oh yes, I'm deputy sheriff in about fifteen or twenty different counties in the United States and a member of the National Sheriffs Association. As a matter of fact, I'm Life Member No. 20. I helped finance the Sheriffs Association when it was on shaky legs at the start."

"Well good; it's great work, Marsh, and you've done great work here with your guns and you will in the future. And we'd like to thank you a lot for letting us bother you here this afternoon and we'd like to hear from you from time to time."

"Come out any time."

"O.K. We want to wish you good luck on your television appearance next week. I think it's on NBC, if you will pardon the expression right here, on *We the People* so, if you have a television set, be sure to watch next Friday night for *We the People*."

Earnings and Taxes

David Marshall Williams, ex-moonshiner, ex-convict and burgeoning weapons inventor, in 1929 returned home to a small farmhouse with but a few dollars in his pocket. Too proud to ask for a loan from the family and determined to make it on his own, he established a tiny shop in an abandoned shed at the rear of his mother's home and continued his weapons development. (Marsh's brother Shell presently lives in his mother's old home.) Working with sweat and determination on bits of iron and steel salvaged from junk piles around the community, his visions became realities.

Williams eventually found a junked lathe, minus the engine, and brought this to his shop (Photo 43), although there was hardly room in the shop for him and the lathe. He restored this dilapidated piece of equipment to excellent working order, but had no engine to pull the leather belts that drove the lathe. This posed little problem for Marshall Williams, one who always found ways to accomplish that which he desired. Whenever he would see a laborer on the farm "who appeared to be standing around idle," Williams would herd him into the shop and put him to the task of pulling the belts by hand. This task was not restricted to the farm labor; it also fell on the shoulders of a couple of Marshall Williams' brothers. It was not long before laborers, brothers and friends learned to stay clear of the shop area whenever Williams was working there.

Looking back to those days when Williams began operating his shop, Miss Maggie recalled, "I never disturbed Marsh. Many a night he worked through the entire night on a project. He missed meals and many nights did not sleep. He had a small cot in the shop and often, when exhausted, he would stretch out on that cot and rest a few hours before returning to his work. He was obsessed with the idea of completing a project once he started it. He seemed supremely happy at his work and often whistled tunes as he worked."

It was during those times that Marshall developed and perfected the .22 conversion of the .30 caliber machine gun and the conversion of the .45 automatic to .22 caliber.

With completed and perfected inventions in hand, Marshall Williams made visits to the War Department to show them. It was during one of these visits that he met a fellow who gained his deep admiration and respect, a man now internationally known in the field of weapons development, General (then Major) Julian Hatcher.

Photo 43. Shell Williams looks over the shoulder of his brother Carbine working at the lathe. All of the Williamses had good working knowledge of weapons and machinery and assisted the inventor whenever the need arose.

General Hatcher described Williams as "a natural, a mechanical genius." Williams impressed not only General Hatcher (who later autographed Williams' copy of his own book as "the greatest inventor in world"), but he impressed military Ordnance personnel and manufacturers of arms as well.

It was at this point that Marshall Williams learned that the world of business was not a place for a naive country boy with limited formal education. There was no room in the business world for sympathy to his situation. There was no generosity, no quarter shown — only an apparent determination on the part of all concerned to get whatever possible out of this genius as cheaply as possible.

Marshall Williams was never adequately compensated for his inventions. The .22 caliber machine gun, for example, saved the United States government fifty million dollars the first year of its use in training. Williams, utilizing machine guns that the government had in storage, made minor alterations and incorporated his floating chamber. His efforts provided a better weapon, a much more economical weapon and, in the end, gave this country a better trained soldier in a shorter training period.

Here is how he was repaid for his contributions to our military effort.

On the 11th day of November 1931, Marshall Williams entered into a contract with the United States of America (contract W-ORD-142) which read: "The contractor shall modify one Browning water-cooled machine gun caliber .30, model 1917, and adapt it to the use of caliber .22 long rifle ammunition of standard, commercial, smokeless types. The modification shall be based on the 'movable chamber' principle as embodied in application for United States letters patent No. 514252 filed by the contractor as shown in a model semi-automatic rifle caliber .22 submitted by contractor to the Ordnance Department for trial and examination.

"The United States will furnish the contractor, free of charge, one Browning water-cooled machine gun caliber

.30, model 1917, with tripod, together with such additional spare parts as may be necessary for the purpose of modification, also three caliber .22 gun barrels. Title to all this property shall remain in the United States.

"Payment will be made upon delivery and acceptance of the completed modified Browning machine gun. The United States shall have the right to manufacture or have manufactured caliber .22 machine gun embodying any feature included in the modified machine gun herein contracted for, or any improvements thereof, where are now or may hereafter be covered by United States letters patent or any extensions thereof upon payment of *a royalty of two dollars per gun up to and including five thousands guns, after which all royalty payments will cease.*" [author's italics]

Williams accepted this contract and the weapon was developed and delivered to the Army in short order. On March 5, 1932, David Marshall Williams entered into another government contract which read as follows: "Make the necessary modifications on five Browning water-cooled machine guns caliber .30, model 1917, to adapt them to operate for full automatic fire and belt-fed using caliber .22 long rifle cartridges of standard commercial smokeless type. The rate of fire of these guns, as modified, shall be between four hundred and four hundred and fifty rounds per minute. Each gun will be required to fire one thousand rounds as an acceptance test. There must be no breakages of major parts and not over five percent malfunctions with any gun.

"The contractor will furnish with each gun two one hundred round belts adapted for caliber .22 ammunition. The United States will furnish the contractor, free of charge, five Browning water-cooled machine guns caliber .30, model 1917, together with such additional spare parts as may be necessary for the purpose of modification, also ten caliber .22 barrels. Title to all this property shall remain with the United States. The United States will also furnish for use in testing these guns ten thousand rounds of caliber .22 long rifle ammunition. Delivery shall be made within five months. Payment will be made upon delivery and acceptance of the completed modified guns. It is hereby certified that in the event award is made to the undersigned, the articles or materials furnished the United States will be of the growth production of manufacture of the United States, except as noted below or otherwise indicated in their bid." Author's note: Carbine Williams wrote upon my copy, "No other one or company made a bid as they did not know how to get the great operating energy from a small caliber cartridge. My floating chamber was the answer. It is the only known way of getting great operating energy from the small cartridge at this time."

The government paid Williams a mere $500 per gun, or a total of $2,500, for this work. In both examples noted, payments included his time, materials, transportation and all operating costs. Upon delivery, these weapons operated perfectly and were well received, and the government decided to enter into the production of these machine guns and to distribute them throughout the training fields of the military forces.

In March of 1932, Williams was awarded a contract by the Ordnance Department to convert .30 caliber machine guns to .22 caliber. He was to receive royalties at the rate of $2 per gun. The contract provided, however, that royalties cease after five thousand guns were made.

To develop, design and produce the first machine gun, Marshall Williams received $1,000. To build five additional guns for the Army, he received $2,500. The total royalties paid on the remaining five thousand guns produced was $10,000. Thus, the inventor received a total of $13,500 for his invention, labor, material and transportation. Yet, this invention resulted in a savings of $25 on every one thousand cartridges expended by troops.

In a nutshell, every time the weapon fired eighty cartridges, the government saved enough money to pay Marshall Williams his $2 royalty on the machine gun that he invented. (As an example of the vast quantities of ammunition purchased by the government, simultaneous with the presentation of the conversion of the .30 caliber machine gun to caliber .22, several manufacturing companies *each* received orders for ninety million .22 cartridges.)

In addition to the .22 caliber machine gun, Marshall Williams also introduced his conversion of the .45 automatic handgun to .22 caliber. As every military man knows the .45 automatic was also used in military training. At the request of Colt Firearms Company, Williams went to Hartford and designed a slightly modified and improved model of the weapon. The developmental work required Williams to spend a full year at the Colt plant. The results were very similar to those with the War Department. Colt gave Carbine Williams a royalty of forty cents each for a pistol that sold for about $50 to the government. This pistol, advertised as Colt's Ace, was used by civilian shooters as well as the military of the United States, resulting in great savings in ammunition expenses through utilization of caliber .22 ammunition.

The following is a letter dated April 25, 1934, from the War Department, Office of the Chief of Ordnance, Washington, D.C. This letter was addressed to Mr. David M. Williams, Godwin, North Carolina.

Dear Mr. Williams:

I am directed by the Chief of Ordnance to inform you that this office has received a letter from Springfield Armory in regard to the utilization of your services there in connection with the work on the caliber .22 machine guns and have been advised that the work has not progressed to the point where your services could be advantageously used at this time.

The U.S. machine gun caliber .22 M-1, which is now being tooled up for production at Springfield Armory, follows entirely the design submitted by you, with the exception of some minor changes made for the purpose of facilitating production and which in no way can affect functioning of the mechanism. At the present time the design of tools, jigs and fixtures in accordance with the design of the weapon has not yet been completed. The tools are being manufactured as rapidly as facilities will permit.

It is planned to manufacture, using the production tools and equipment, a sufficient quantity of components to assemble ten of these guns before proceeding with the production of all guns now on order. It is essential that this be done in order to test the interchangeability and the design. It is very probable that when assembly is undertaken of these first production models it will be found necessary to make minor changes in order to have the mechanism perform satisfactorily. It is considered that it would be advantageous to have you at Springfield Armory at that time for approximately a three month period.

It is expected that the first production models will be ready for assembly about the first of July but no definite date can be stated at this time. This office will be advised by Springfield Armory of the definite date when this assembly will begin in order that we may communicate with you. It will therefore be necessary for this office to defer its attempts to secure the temporary appointment for you at Springfield Armory until about the first of July, or when definitely advised by the Armory.

It is hoped that this will give you information as to the situation and when definitely informed regarding the date the guns will be assembled this office will communicate with you further.

Very truly yours,
R. H. Lee, Major
Ordnance Department, Assistant

The letter is undersigned by J. S. Crawford, captain of Ordnance. With his usual attention to detail, and with a degree of satisfaction, Williams wrote across the bottom of this letter: "I did go to Springfield Armory and stayed there quite a while."

It was not only the Ordnance Department and the manufacturing companies that tried to get as much as possible for as little as possible, and with little consideration for the inventor. Carbine Williams' fame had ebbed and after he had returned home with fifty-nine major patents, the United States government in 1948 filed a lawsuit against him claiming he owed more than $156,900 in back taxes. (Between the years 1954 and 1963 alone, he paid more than $84,000 in taxes.) The major portion of the tax claimed was based on Williams' having received $234,001.46 in 1942 from the Winchester Arms Company for developing the caliber .30 M-1 carbine. This payment was based on the initial government contract of $886,000 granted to Winchester for production of the weapon.

Contrary to popular belief, Marshall Williams did not receive a royalty on each carbine. During World War II, alone, more than eight million carbines were produced. Had Marshall Williams received even one dollar per carbine, he would have been a multimillionaire at that time. He was paid a total of $234,001.46 for the weapon, and of this the government initially took a sizable percentage for taxes. Many companies across the United States manufactured the carbine. As noted earlier, so many were manufacturing it that a coordinating committee for the manufacture of carbines was formed. Williams did not receive one penny from any of these producing companies.

The tax hassle between David Marshall "Carbine" Williams and the U.S. government was later written up as an important tax case example. The case consumed hundreds of pages with references to countless tax regulations and acknowledgements of the opinions of some of the most prominent figures in the field of tax law.

Before detailing here excerpts from this famous case, I carefully note that Marshall Williams and his lawyers won the "battle" of this tax case although the inventor lost the overall "war," in that for the rest of his life he and his wife and brothers were continually harassed by the Internal Revenue Service by correspondence and through endless visits by agents of the tax department. (The initial debate was to decide if the income from his invention was to be classified as "ordinary income" or "capital gain.")

DAVID WILLIAMS VS. THE UNITED STATES
In the United States Court of Claims.
No. 47736. Decided June 6, 1949.

Compensation for services rendered: Inventor: Income and tax related to time when work done — An inventor who worked on an invention until 1931, but who did not receive the income from it until 1942, was allowed to relate the income and tax to the time when the work which produced the income was done. The government was not correct in relating the income and tax to some other arbitrarily fixed and irrelevant period . . . .

In May 1939, [David Marshall Williams] became a salaried employee at New Haven, Connecticut, of the Winchester Repeating Arms Company, a division of Western Cartridge Company, hereinafter referred to as 'Winchester,' at an annual salary of $5,000, which was later increased to $5,500 or $6,000. His duties as an employee of Winchester were to develop new guns and new gun mechanisms. Under the terms of his employment any patentable inventions which he might develop would belong to Winchester. . . .

During the years he was engaged in farming, plaintiff earned very little income and filed no income tax returns. After becoming a salaried employee, plaintiff filed income tax returns for the years 1939 to 1943, inclusive, with the Collector of Internal Revenue for the District of Connecticut. . . .

By agreements of November 11, 1931, and March 14, 1932, plaintiff granted a license to the United States Government to make and use or have made and used on .22-caliber machine guns the short stroke piston device or vibrator, a form of which is described in United States Patent No. 2,090, 656, in exchange for royalty payments. On April 30, 1934, plaintiff granted an exclusive license to the Colt Patent Fire Arms Manufacturing Company to manufacture, use, and sell automatic pistols with right to sublicense others to manufacture, use, and sell automatic pistols containing the invention covered by Patent No. 2,090,656 in exchange for royalty payments. By agreement of November 1, 1939, plaintiff granted an exclusive license to Remington Arms Company, Inc., to make, use, and sell sporting shoulder rifles embodying the invention covered by Patent No. 2,090,656 in exchange for royalty payments.

On September 9, 1940, plaintiff granted an exclusive license to Winchester, except for rights previously granted by plaintiff as shown in the preceding finding, to make, use, sell, have made, and rights to license others for certain specified types of military and sporting firearms containing a vibrator or actuator in the form of a short stroke piston, as described in Patent No. 2,090,656, in exchange for a royalty payable to plaintiff on the basis of the value of each gun manufactured containing plaintiff's invention.

In March 1942, Winchester granted royalty free to the United States Government a nonexclusive, irrevocable right to manufacture and use, or to cause to be manufactured and used by others for Government purposes, a light weight military carbine officially designated Carbine Caliber .30M1 which included plaintiff's invention covered by Patent No. 2,090,656 in consideration of payment by the Government to Winchester of a lump sum of $886,000. On March 19, 1942, plaintiff entered into an agreement with Winchester consenting to the foregoing contractual arrangement between Winchester and the United States and agreeing to accept 26.411 percent of the lump-sum payment of $886,000 provided therein *in lieu of all royalties to which he would otherwise be entitled* [author's italics] under the license agreement of September 9, 1940, referred to in the preceding finding.

With the exception of Patent No. 2,090,656, the patents and patent applications listed under the name of Williams in the contract between Winchester and the United States Government and attached to the contract between Winchester and plaintiff dated March 19, 1942, *all belonged to Winchester* [author's italics]. . . .

Pursuant to the agreement of March 19, 1942, referred to in finding 9, Winchester paid plaintiff the sum of $234,001.46 in the year 1942, which sum represented a royalty payment for the use of plaintiff's device covered by Patent No. 2,090,656. That sum had no connection with plaintiff's duties as an employee of Winchester. In addition to the foregoing amount of $234.001.46, plaintiff received royalty income under the licenses granted to use his invention covered by Patent No. 2,090,656 as follows:

Year	Source	Amount
1939	Colt Patent Firearms Manufacturing Co .	$ 250.00
1940	Colt Patent Firearms Manufacturing Co .	250.00
	Winchester	3,000.00
1941	Colt Patent Firearms Manufacturing Co.	329.60
	Ordnance Department, U.S. Army	534.00
	Remington Arms Company	3,297.78
1942	War Department, U.S. Army	3,474.00
	Remington Arms Co.	8,074.59
	Colt Patent Firearms Manufacturing Co.	589.20

From the date of the receipt of the lump sum payment of $234,001.46 in 1942 to September 8, 1948, the date of the trial of the case, plaintiff received no royalty income from the invention covered by Patent No. 2,090,656.

Plaintiff paid amounts on account of the tax liability shown on his income tax returns for 1942 and 1943 as follows:

Apr. 1, 1943 . . . . $24,714,84
Aug. 4, 1943 . . . . 24,714.84
Oct. 14, 1943 . . . . 24,335.45
Dec. 29, 1943 . . . . 24,335.44

Through withholding of income and victory tax by his employer during 1943 . . . . . 791.06

Total   98,891.63

Plaintiff claimed a refund of $254.42 on his income tax return for 1943. That sum was refunded to him and was the only refund made to plaintiff on account of his income taxes for the years 1942 and 1943.

Plaintiff's income tax returns for the years 1942 and 1943 correctly reflected the amount of income which plaintiff received in those years.

On March 15, 1945, plaintiff filed a claim for refund of income taxes for the year 1942 in the amount of $45,252.60 on the ground that 'Patents sold in 1942 should have been considered as Capital Gain instead of Ordinary Income.' On March 15, 1946, plaintiff filed a claim for refund of income taxes for the year 1943 in the amount of $68,977.66, amending and supplementing the claim filed for 1942, on the ground that the gross income received by plaintiff in 1942 from his invention should be apportioned ratably over the period of thirty-six months prior to February 7, 1931, when the period of work on the invention terminated and the tax computed at the rates in effect during those years, and that the overstatement of tax for the taxable year 1942 resulted in overstatement of the tax for the taxable year 1943 under the Current Tax Payment Act of 1943. . . .

In a ninety-day letter dated June 25, 1948, the Commissioner of Internal Revenue notified plaintiff that the claims for refund referred to in the preceding finding would be disallowed. In connection with that disallowance, the Commissioner reduced the royalty payment of $234,001.46 received by plaintiff from Winchester in 1942 by $26,000 expenses in connection with foreign rights and further by expenses incurred in obtaining the patent, thus determining $201,601.46 as the net amount received by plaintiff for the use of his invention covered by Patent No. 2,090,656. In addition, the Commissioner, purporting to act in accordance with the provision of Section 107(b) of the Internal Revenue Code, allocated that net amount of $201,601.46 in equal installments to the thirty-six months immediately preceding the close of the calendar year 1942. Through his application of Section 107 (b), the Commissioner determined plaintiff's total tax liability for the years 1940, 1941, and 1942, in the amount of $114,783.32. To that tax the Commissioner added an unforgiven part of plaintiff's 1943 tax liability as provided in Section 6 (b) of the Current Tax

Payment Act of 1943, making a total tax due as determined by him of $115,005.47. Since plaintiff's income tax return filed March 15, 1944, for the year 1943, reported a tax liability of only $98,637.21, the Commissioner determined a deficiency in income and victory tax against plaintiff for 1943 of $16,368.26, which tax has not been paid by plaintiff.

Conclusion of Law

Upon the foregoing special findings of fact which are made a part of the judgment herein, the court concludes as a matter of law that the plaintiff is entitled to recover. . . .

It was the conclusion of the court that Marshall Williams was entitled to a refund. To back their decision, Judges Howell, Whitaker and Littleton, and Chief Judge Jones, in their summation completely concurred in their findings on behalf of Williams and provided the Internal Revenue Service with endless dissertation which referred to:

1) An Opinion by Judge Madden
2) An explanation of Section 107, Compensation for Services Rendered for a Period of Thirty-six Months or More and Back Pay
3) An extract from (b) of Section 107, Patents and Copyright, Inc.
4) A reference to Section 220, Revenue Act of 1939
5) A reference to Section 107, Compensation for Services Rendered for a Period of Five Years or More
6) An Explanation of Subsections (a) and (b) of Section 107

Further, in their summary of their decision, the judges explained that a change made in the language of the bill by the Senate might have been made primarily to limit the period of computation to the actual time of work on the invention. They further noted that Congress may well not have foreseen the unusual situation which Williams' case presented and, for this reason, did not clearly answer the question presented.

The case and trial was concluded as far as the Williams family was concerned and as far as the judges were concerned, but was *not* concluded in the minds and hearts of the Internal Revenue Service officials. Marshall Williams, his wife and family were to be questioned and harassed for the rest of their life. As late as 1965 the United States Treasury Department wrote the following letter to Carbine's brother, Gordon M. Williams, who at that time was very close to his brother and acting as his administrator. (Carbine was at this time ill and his temperament such that it was best that he not try to deal with these government agents personally.)

Dear Sir:

The following list represents all delinquent income tax accounts in this office, reflecting both the amount assessed and the amount paid as of this date. The figures are as follows:

ASSESSED AMOUNT $156,966.44
TOTAL AMOUNT PAID INCLUDING
    INTEREST 84,405.68
BALANCE DUE $72,560.76

UNITED STATES
TREASURY DEPARTMENT

To determine if his repeated tax problems had shaken his faith in America, I asked Williams:

"Marsh, you have contributed greatly to the defense of America. You have been 'had' on many royalties by many companies. You are penniless today, yet the government still hounds you for taxes. How do you feel toward this country under these circumstances?"

"Hell, Ross, I love this country," he replied. "I'd do anything for it. If I had a corner of Ft. Knox, I'd give it to 'em. But I don't have anything left. I'm tired and I'm old. And all I ask is that they let me alone the rest of my days."

Photo 1-15   "Carbine" and the author share a lighter moment in his workshop (R.E. Beard).

CHAPTER 11
Inventions Other Than Firearms

Carbine always stressed that he never sat down and worked at an idea. New ideas for inventions just popped into his mind at random. But there were rare exceptions. Many times out of love for his Maggie, Williams set his mind to make items that would benefit her. Many were extremely successful and are heretofore unknown to the outside world.

A Clothesline that Will Not Sag

Just as her husband, Miss Maggie is a perfectionist, especially when it comes to cleanliness of the clothes she washes. While hanging out her laundry one day, she noted to Marsh that as she added more and more wet articles to her clothesline, it sagged until some of her beautifully cleaned wash touched the ground. Naturally she had to rewash some of them. Sitting there looking at the sagging line, Marshall Williams decided that the problem could be remedied and went to his shop to give it serious thought.

Late that afternoon Williams reappeared in the backyard equipped with an assortment of material and tools, including a rather strong and very long length of stainless wire, several two-by-fours, some pulleys, a large concrete block and wire staples, plus his hammer and pliers.

First, he attached the end of the wire to one of the pulleys and carefully twisted it for permanent anchorage.

Then exactly halfway between the two buildings to which the line ends were to be attached, Williams firmly anchored in the ground an upright two-by-four approximately five feet long. He then threaded the other end of this wire through a staple driven into the top of the median timber. Next, he attached a pulley to the second building and bolted to it another two-by-four, allowing it to move somewhat like a windshield wiper blade to the side of the building. To this he strung the clothesline wire and counter-weighted it with the concrete block. The block hanging free caused the clothesline to become quite taut.

"Maggie, bring me a load of wash," Williams ordered.

"Marsh, what do you want with my wash?" she inquired.

"Never you mind, Maggie, just bring it out here," he responded.

With the tranquil manner characteristic of Miss Maggie, she brought her carefully washed sheets, shirts and other garments to Marsh. Quickly, eager to try his invention, Marsh began to hang out clothes. As pound after pound of wet clothing was added to the line, the line remained arrow straight, countered by the weight of the block.

Delighted, Miss Maggie complimented her inventor husband on his ingenious rig, and in return she received one of those very rare, deep, warm smiles that included both love for his wife and the inner satisfaction of seeing an idea become reality. In keeping with the quality of his weapons, this line continues to stand arrow straight and has never allowed Miss Maggie's clothes to touch the ground.

A Can Opener

Another invention by Williams is equally unusual. As time passed, Maggie began to suffer with arthritis in her hands and fingers and it became difficult to punch a can opener into the lid of a can of milk or juice. Noticing this and unable to bear watching his Maggie suffer, Marshall

Williams went to his shop, selected a special piece of steel, turned and fashioned it like an ice pick blade and sharpened the tip. He fashioned a handle that looked very much like a door knob, only slightly smaller. In attaching the handle to the blade of the can opener, Williams applied the floating chamber principle, utilizing a small spring between the punch and handle.

With this unique invention, Miss Maggie simply uses the palm of her hand to apply the slightest pressure to the big, oval knob handle. The movement of approximately five-thousandths of an inch does the rest. The sharp punch, when activated, quickly and expertly pierces the can with absolutely no pain to Miss Maggie's hands. The can opener is still in use.

Little things which were practical and which simplified everyday living were frequently introduced by Marshall Williams. Always interested in knowing the whereabouts of his Maggie if she left while he was working, Williams took a simple clothespin some thirty years ago and carefully nailed it to the top of the fence post at the gate to his yard to hold his wife's notes and messages. Clothespins have been utilized in numerous such commercial devices in recent years. Even Carbine Williams never thought to seek a patent on such a simple contrivance.

A Door Stop

Almost daily Marshall Williams would make the long walk from his shop to the house, carrying weapons or parts in various stages of completion to show Maggie (or to sit and observe while eating), looking for an idea or a new way of accomplishing something. Many times he had both hands full and could not make the door stay open, causing him to have to yell for Miss Maggie. This was time consuming and, too, it bothered his wife, especially if she was at the other end of the house.

Again Williams applied his genius. He watched for days just how far family members normally opened the door and, having determined this, rigged a simple wooden lever that would automatically drop into place when the door was opened wider than usual. Thus, the door was held open so that, in Williams' words, "I could get my weapons in the house without having them knocked out of my hands by that damned door, and so that the door would not slam me in the butt every time I entered." This device, too, is still in use at the Williams' home.

A Better Mousetrap

Once on a visit to Carbine's home, I walked into the shop and, even while being greeted, noticed an excitement in the air and twinkle in Williams' eye that told me something was happening — or was going to happen. Knowing Williams on occasion could be a practical joker, I was uneasy about what was going to happen. I did not have long to wait and this time it was not a practical joke.

"Ross, I'm told that the quickest way to fame and is to invent a better mousetrap. Do you agree?" Williams inquired.

"Carbine, I believe that you have left your footprints in that road to fame and fortune long ago," I retorted.

"I know, but maybe I done it the wrong way," he continued. "Maybe I should have followed the mousetrap course and invented a better mousetrap."

I continued to sense under that joking an excitement that was real and my curiosity became unbearable: "O.K., Carbine, come on out with it. What the hell are you up to? What's with this better mousetrap bit?"

From under the workbench Marshall Williams produced a box, and when he opened it he proudly and seriously announced, "Ross, I've done it. I've invented a better mouse or rat trap. See here? Let me explain." He reached in the box and removed a large rat trap.

A quick examination revealed that he had not altered the principle of the old rat trap but he had added two innovations that did, indeed, make it a better and most unusual trap. First, Williams had developed a method by which to set the sensitivity of the trigger (like a set trigger) with the simple turn of a screw. So sensitive was this setting mechanism that a breath exhaled on the trigger would cause it to snap shut. Or it could be set so that only heavy pressure on the trigger would activate the trap.

Next, Williams placed the trap on the floor of the shop and set the trigger to "ultra-sensitive." He then asked me to move the trap over to the other side of the shop, "but be careful not to set it off."

My immediate response was, "If you think I am going to pick up that trap in my hand and move it, as sensitive as it is set, you have another thought coming."

Marshall Williams smashed his broad hand down on my back and, laughing, said, "Ross, that is exactly what I thought you would say. You have allowed me to make my point about the second part of this better mousetrap. She has a safety for moving it without triggering the trap." With this, Marshall Williams walked up to the trap and, with the edge of the sole of his wide brogan, depressed a small piece of metal on the side of the trap. A safety latch efficiently flipped into position, rendering the trap harmless.

I could only smile and say, "Damn it, Carbine, you *have* actually built a better mousetrap." Who knows, maybe the better mousetrap with be another factor in Williams' continued walk up the road of fame.

Photo 2-43a "Carbine" Williams giving a demonstration of his new .22 cal. machine gun to the U.S. Army. He and the author sewed the belt from venetian blind straps! (R.E. Beard).

CHAPTER 12
Visit to a Gun Show

I made many attempts to convince Marshall Williams that the world of gun collectors would delight in meeting him and seeing his weapons. The inventor had long before decided that his tranquil little farm was where he preferred to remain the rest of his life, and often refused to open letters or to see visitors. At length, he agreed to appear at a gun show in North Carolina where we would jointly display items related to his inventions. I excitedly selected weapons from my collection that would form the backdrop for the display of his inventor's models.

A friend in Camden, South Carolina, Charles Wilson, was also an avid gun collector and great admirer of Carbine Williams. I received permission from Carbine to invite Charlie to attend the show with us. Charlie was delighted and before daylight on a Saturday morning we departed Camden for Godwin to pick up Carbine and his weapons.

Upon arrival at the inventor's home, introductions were made and, typical of Williams, he took care of first things first. Getting his weapons loaded in the car was a definite first, and meeting and getting to know Charlie was second.

Shortly after we arrived, Williams popped up with an unnerving comment: "Ross, that fellow looks like a damned guy I should have shot years ago. Looks a plumb damned lot like him." As we began loading the car, I assured Williams that he was A-O.K. and not the same guy. Reluctantly, Williams handed Charles two Caledonia prison knives to put in the car. Looking him dead in the eye, he said, "Fellow, you be damned sure these get in the car." Charlie, having been carefully briefed for days on what to do and what not to do, promptly took these knives to the car *but* laid them on the rear fender beside the trunk until the heavier machine guns and rifles were loaded. Seeing this, I quietly picked up the knives and hid them under the seat of the car (letting Carbine see what I was doing but not Charles). We dashed around completing the loading of the weapons and off we departed for the gun show.

On arrival, we were greeted by a most obnoxious individual who, unfortunately, was in charge of and master of ceremonies for the show. He was a loudmouth and several times came close to meeting his Maker by his flippant and uncalled for comments to and about Carbine Williams. It took much effort on my part to keep Carbine from settling the matter with him then and there. To add fuel to the fire, a disreputable gun dealer took Williams aside and gave him several drinks, knowing that once drinking, Williams would not stop, and perhaps hoping in the back of his mind that he could relieve Williams of some treasured item. (He was removed from the show and barred from appearing again.)

Charlie, watching all of this, was getting more and more nervous, for Williams was ordering him about and still commenting that he looked like a guy he should have shot years before. After we set up and identified the displays, I called Charlie aside and said, "Charlie, you carried Williams' knives to the car. You did put them in the trunk, didn't you?" Charles looked at the display and the knives were not there—only the name tags. Being a bright young man, he remembered instantly that he had laid them on the fender until the heavier things were loaded. I assured him that I had not put them in the trunk and surmised that they must have blown off somewhere along the road as we drove to the show.

Before I could stop him, Charlie, pale and totally unnerved by this thought, raced to a phone and called Mrs. Williams to see if the knives had been found in the yard after we departed. Mrs. Williams' negative response added to his agitation. Charlie was fully aware of what would happen if Williams found he had carelessly lost the treasured knives made in Caledonia prison. Charlie is not a man who scares easily, but there was little question in his mind that the best thing he could do was disappear from the face of the earth immediately.

Unable to contain myself any longer, I owned up to my doings as Williams laughed wildly. Charlie invented a few new words that best described me at that moment. Although he did not think the incident funny at all, Charlie's relief was so great that he finally calmed down sufficiently to participate in the remainder of the show.

We won first place, which delighted Carbine, and again he found a "friend" who gave him another drink of liquor. It was midnight before the weapons were all accounted for and carefully loaded in the trunk of the car. After much conversation, we got Carbine into the back seat and headed for home.

In the excitement of preparing to leave the show, I failed to check the gas gauge. About eight miles out of Pacolet, South Carolina, I noticed that the indicator was past the empty mark. Now, if you really want to see a man upset, run out of gas with Carbine Williams aboard. Perfectionist that he was, he could not abide such a trifling incident. Frankly, I was sweating blood hoping that at 1:00 a.m. I could find some station open. At the moment the car sputtered and started to die, we saw at the bottom of a hill a decrepit station with one gas pump lighted, and rocked the car sufficiently to roll the last few feet to the pump.

The station was open and, as I tried to find the attendant, Carbine went inside looking for a restroom. Thinking that he was headed for another drink, Charlie and I rushed for the entrance to intercept him.

As we burst through the door, we could see that a fracas was in the making. A large intoxicated man wearing bib overalls had stepped in the aisle in front of Williams and, with hands on hips, said, "Ol' man, where the hell do you think you're going?" As fast as the wink of an eye, Marshall Williams whipped out not one but two .45 automatics and, with hammers back, answered in a low, deadly growl, including a profane description of the man, "I'm going to the toilet—over you or around you." With this, he placed both automatic barrels to the man's mouth and added, "I'm Carbine Williams."

The juke box was shut off and the room became totally silent; the man facing the weapons turned white as a sheet and sweat poured down his face and dripped from his chin. Stammering, he managed to say, "Honest, sir, Mr. Williams, sir, I didn't know who you were, sir, uh," and then blurted out loudly, "Sir, honest, I'm a convict too." With this, Williams, calmly, without a word, lowered the hammers, walked to the restroom and, after some minutes, walked back out to find the room still stone silent and the man still standing in the same place.

Williams walked up to the man and said, "Fellow, you had better know who you are bulling up to, for hell, man, had I not been in a plumb good mood, I woulda shot you without even introducing myself." With this, both of us, still frozen in the corner, began to breathe again and the room became active as patrons requested Carbine's autograph and offered to buy him drinks. We spent the next two hours trying to get Williams back into the car.

Around 3:30 a.m. we were rolling again and Williams was holding forth in the back seat. Charlie and I were not having much to say about this time, for we were both unnerved and badly in need of a little rest. We had spent a total of thirty-nine hours with the Tiger of Cumberland County; he had not slowed down for a minute and no let-up was in sight. Finally, we arrived at his home near Godwin, managed to unload and again account for all weapons, got Carbine in the house and began our three-hour ride home.

CHAPTER 13
Mrs. Spot

If I were to select any single object that brought great happiness to Carbine Williams, I would, without reservation, select a beautiful puppy named Spot. She's an old lady now, quite happy to lie at Mrs. Williams' feet and enjoy the warmth of the little stove. A dignified lady, gracious to old friends, Spot is still capable of a wag of the tail and a little friendly yowling if talked to. Yet, as old as she is, she is still capable of bristling the fur on her back and giving a low warning growl if a stranger approaches.

When Spot was a small puppy, brother Gordon brought her to Carbine's shop and it was love at first sight. Much of the day was spent petting and talking to "Miss Spot," as she was known then, and in following days you did not see Carbine Williams without seeing a black and white blur dashing around his feet or darting into the fields in mock hunting, and running back to the protection of Carbine if too big a bird happened to fly up.

This playfulness came close to causing the demise of Miss Spot, for one morning as Gordon was passing the shop, plowing with a huge tractor with many discs behind, Miss Spot darted between the tractor and the discs and was badly cut on the hip. Excitement and action prevailed, for when you hurt Miss Spot, you may as well have injured Carbine himself.

Plowing stopped, Gordon ran for a pick-up truck and Carbine Williams gently held this puppy in his massive hands, softly talking to her, reassuring her that she would be O.K. Following a frenzied trip to the veterinarian, where the dog received extensive stitches, Carbine calmed down after being assured that Miss Spot would live and be well again soon. Gordon was equally relieved, for he, too, knew how important Miss Spot was to his brother.

On return from the hospital, Miss Spot thrived on the special attentions she received, and it was during this period of recovery that her training began. In my opinion, it was also at this time that the puppy began to understand Carbine Williams' language and moods.

As weeks passed, I became more and more amazed at her understanding of her master. Carbine would fill her plate and place it on the back porch but, to my disbelief, Miss Spot would not go to or touch that food, even if several hours passed, unless Carbine would say, "O.K., Miss Spot, eat your dinner." She also knew that Carbine followed an exact time schedule for his daily trip to the shop, and was always standing at the door waiting to accompany him there. She had learned to walk at the side of or just behind her master.

On visits to the Williams' home, we often drove my car to the workshop, carrying weapons or other items. Miss Spot immediately learned how to get on the floor of the front seat of the car at such an angle as to allow foot room for Carbine and foot room for me to operate the car. This, from the first trip, was her spot and she refused to relinquish it to a second passenger.

On very warm days Miss Spot preferred the coolness under the workshop. One day while I was visiting Carbine he pulled out a mouth organ, an instrument I previously did not know he played. The second he blew the first note, Miss Spot's tail began hitting the sills as she made a mad dash for the shop. Once inside she sat on Carbine's feet and added her melodious howls to the music being played.

I once received a letter from Carbine with news that Miss Spot had run away and "gotten married." The proud mother of cuddlesome puppies, she was from that day forth referred to as *Mrs.* Spot.

Not one to be left out of the action, Mrs. Spot "assisted" Carbine one morning when he was autographing the limited edition pages of this book. Failing to get the attention she felt she deserved, she stepped in the ink, turned over the bottle and promptly "autographed" a page of her own, much to the delight of Carbine.

For years Mrs. Spot was constantly at the side of her master, involved in every move and in every mood of Carbine. As time passed and as Carbine became very ill and ceased to be able to recognize his friends or his beloved Mrs. Spot, she, too, seemed to understand and accept the change. She never failed to show great interest when Carbine returned home from a visit to the hospital, only now she stayed at Miss Maggie's feet, quietly watching. She no longer approached Carbine, almost as if she were afraid she would disturb him. She no longer went to the door to greet him, nor did she follow him to the door when he returned to the hospital. She was responsible for and to Mrs. Williams now, and she accepted this responsibility to remain behind to protect her. In turn, not once following Carbine's illness did he ever acknowledge that Mrs. Spot was anywhere around. However, Mrs. Spot never turned away nor forgot Carbine's friends. Whenever I arrived, I was given a warm, tail-wagging, "talking" greeting.

Photo 2-41a David M. Williams at home in North Carolina
(R.E. Beard).

CHAPTER 14
Another Viewpoint

There are always two sides to every story, especially when a murder charge is involved and, regardless of time, it is natural that grief and bitterness still exist. I was able to meet and interview Ellen (Mrs. George B.) Stevens, daughter of slain Deputy Sheriff Al J. Pate. She was most gracious, exceptionally courteous, genuine in her beliefs concerning the murder and trial and candid in her response to questions. I would be remiss in my responsibility to present all known facts if I failed to include her opinions concerning the fatal shooting.

Interview with Mrs. George B. Stevens
October 1, 1966

"Mrs. Stephens, how long was Deputy Sheriff Al Pate an officer?"

"From 1902 until he was killed in 1921."

"When Sheriff Pate was killed in this raid, what age was he?"

"Sixty-three. He was in perfect health."

"Did you live here in Fayetteville then?"

"Yes."

"About what size man was he in height, weight and so forth? Was he a big man?"

"No, he was medium-sized, I suppose."

"I would like to know, prior to this last raid on Williams' still, if Sheriff Pate ever had the occasion to raid him before? I know that he was making moonshine whiskey before that."

"No, he was asked to make the raid by Sheriff McGeachy."

"Can you remember offhand who the other officers were who were in on this raid when they went in there?"

"Well, Mr. West that drove them was in the car when my father got in, you know. He was shot when he was in the car."

"Well, I wanted to ask, was Sheriff McGeachy there?"

"Yes."

"Your father was deputy sheriff to him, and then Mr. West was driving the car. At the time they went in, I understand there was some shooting and everybody ran. Would you tell me how that happened?"

"There was no one at the still when they went in. They looked in and they couldn't find anyone so my father said, 'Boys, I think we'll just tear up the still, pull up the pump, destroy the mash and go.' It was about 5:30 in the afternoon. So, he got in the car and Mr. West told me then he heard. . .well, he said he had an old model Ford that made so much noise, he looked around and Mr. Pate had slumped over. He said he saw blood running down his shirt, that he had been shot in the back."

"Well now, this is the point that I wanted to get straight. I had heard that he had already finished the destruction of the still and had gotten back in the car."

"He had, and that's when he was shot."

"Well, now, at the time he realized that the sheriff was shot, did Mr. West or anyone see anybody, or know where the shot came from?"

"They did. They said it came from behind a tree and there was a colored man with him [Williams]. That is why he didn't get life. That is, it was circumstantial evidence."

"Well, this is the point that I've never been able to clear up, and this is tremendously important. They realized that it [the shot] came from behind a tree and that there was a colored man with him. In several times that I've interviewed

Carbine. . .(sometimes he's in the mood to talk and sometimes he's not), he has mentioned that there were some Negroes around there that had guns."

"They had this Negro on the stand. The judge asked him what he was being tried for and he said, 'Making bootleg liquor.' He [the judge] said, 'No, you're being tried for murder.' And I've never seen anyone look like he did. He said, 'I'll talk! I'll talk!'. . .So, he talked, and he told that Marshall said to shoot, but he's the one that shot. Marshall did the shooting. And the judge said, 'All right, you can go now. We're through with you.' And this Negro went out of the courthouse and someone told me not long ago that he'd never been seen since. He was frightened. He turned right ashen-looking, he was so frightened. He had no idea that he was being tried for murder. 'Cause he didn't do it. And that was evidence enough right there, and still they said it was circumstantial."

"Well, there was one man at the initial trial who hung that jury. Do you remember who he was?"

"Lives right here, Mr. Spears. Yes, he's a farmer. . . ."

"Well, you told me in talking that you had just been married five days. Were you on your honeymoon at the time that this happened?"

"I was in Arlington, Virginia, and we had just visited the cemetery. We'd come home. My sister-in-law's husband was an Army man, you know. They lived at Ft. Myers, so you can imagine it was a shock. I mean a shock!"

"Well, did they phone you?"

"No, the sheriff wired down there. (The way he worded it was so sweet.) He told me that my father had been shot and killed. Of course, I just lost consciousness. Then I had to come home with all that on me. And the roads, we had no roads like we have now, you know. It took a long time, I'm telling you, to get here."

"Sheriff Pate was one of five brothers, you say?"

"They're all dead."

"Could you remember their names?"

"Oh yes, Uncle Alexander, James, Judson, Hector and Alford. He was the youngest of five. And there were two sisters, Farabe and Eliza."

"You mentioned that you received this wire. By any chance, would you have retained that over these years?"

"I didn't."

"When the sheriff went in to raid the still he was armed. Do you remember what kind of weapon he would have carried?"

"You see, I wasn't here. I didn't know. But I was told that Mr. West said, 'My God! Mr. Pate's been shot!' Sheriff McGeachy came and he was a Christian man; he was never known to curse. They said of all the cursing you ever heard, he did. He was just beside himself. So they took him [my father] to some doctor but he was dead when they arrived there. My father had a beautiful pearl-handled pistol that I wanted so bad. But someone got it before I could. I never knew where it went."

"Was it around here?"

"I went to the courthouse trying to find it and nobody knew where it was. At the time my mother was living, [and] my sisters and my two brothers. They're all dead now, except for one of my sisters."

"Maybe you'd like to comment on some of the events that were highlights during the trial that took place. You mentioned this Negro man who looked ashen when he found out that he was being tried for murder. Were there any high points that you would remember pertaining to your family or the feeling they had during the trial? Or the Williams family? Anything of that nature?"

"Well, you see, my father and Mr. [Claud] Williams, Carbine's father, were friends. He [my father] went up the day before and had dinner with him [Claud Williams] and asked him if he would try to make him [Marshall Williams] mend his ways. He [my father] said, 'I don't want to do anything to him. I don't want to harm him. I don't want to arrest him.' I suppose that he couldn't do anything with him. Anyway, it was raining and Mr. Williams gave my father his raincoat and it was hanging here in this hall when my father was killed. Mr. Williams' raincoat, he wore it. I think that Mr. Williams was a county commissioner at the time. Have you heard that?"

"Yes. He was a very prominent man up there, I understand."

"He was. And my father liked him."

"Well, this is the thing that was so tragic, because I feel from my interviews that the Williams family—father, mother, and all of them—had tried desperately to make Marshall mend his ways."

"Well, that's what my mother said. 'He just got off on the wrong foot,' that's what she said. That's why she signed for them to get him out, you know, to patent his weapon."

"Well now, when the shooting took place and the sheriff was killed, I understand that it was a day or so before they got Marshall Williams."

"Yes, I think it was. He was hiding."

"Have you ever been up there? Up at Godwin, near where he lived?"

"Of course, I've been in Godwin. The woods are so thick and are still that way."

"There was a place up there, I think he called it Five Holly, where this still was located. When did you first see Marshall Williams after the shooting took place? Was it at the jail in Raeford?"

"No."

"At Fayetteville?"

"Well, they moved him from Fayetteville to Raeford for safekeeping."

"Well now, about the family's feeling in that matter: Of course, I know they were shocked and horrified and heartbroken, but were any of the brothers at the point of wanting to go down there and get him and finish him off? How did they feel?"

"Well, they were indignant about it. I guess they must have been, because they were high-tempered; all of them were. They're Scotch-Irish. They were all at the trial. Another thing, the lawyers, all of the lawyers in Fayetteville offered their services free. And Mr. Williams couldn't get one. They wouldn't defend him. I think he went to Dunn."

"His lawyers did come from Dunn."

"Mr. Guy."

"That's right, and then there was another group. There were two groups of lawyers."

"But none of the lawyers charged a thing for the legal services to my family."

"During or before the trial, was there any contact between the Williams family and your family here? I'm just wondering if they ever approached you or made any comment at all."

"Never did."

"When this happened, did this cause handicaps on your family financially?"

"Very much. Back then, there was nothing except half a month's salary given to my mother; no compensation, no insurance, nothing of that kind. He [my father] carried insurance for a while, but it was so high that he couldn't keep it up. And then the pay was very low, very little pay for his services."

"After the trial and after Williams had gone to prison, was there ever any occasion when you saw or heard anything more out of him, or about him, or did anybody ever approach you about him or discuss anything?"

"No, it was kept pretty well shoved aside."

"Your mother ten [actually eight] years later signed papers authorizing his release from prison. Was she approached by the governor of North Carolina or was she approached by the federal government in the interest of defense? How was she approached?"

"She was approached by a letter from the prison. I had gone to work dressmaking. . . .I had to go back to work and my husband was one out of a million to let me go back. You see, I couldn't go with him. He was in the service, you know."

"Was he a career soldier in the service?"

"Yes, he had thirty years with them."

"What was his rank when he retired?"

"He was just a master sergeant. . . .He was from West Virginia. No one else would have considered letting me stay, you know. He was so good to my mother. I went with him for two years and then I had to come home and make a living for her. She couldn't do it. She couldn't get along alone. He said, 'Of course, we cannot make her leave home, because she doesn't want to.' We couldn't take her with us. You can't take somebody else after all of those years."

"That's an understanding man."

"He was one in a million."

"Did your mother, in discussing the signing of this paper. . . , did she make any comment as she signed it, as to why she decided to sign the paper?"

"She said it wouldn't bring him [my father] back for him [Williams] to stay in the prison and, if it would do any good, that she would sign it. If it'd be any good to the government, you know."

"Did she live long enough to see any of the end results of his weapons?"

"Yes. She died in World War II."

"Well then, she must have been extremely gratified to see that such good came from her decision to let him out. It's amazing that a man who could supposedly take a life could also have saved as many as he did with his weapons."

"Yes."

"Do you by any chance have any copies of the form that she signed or anything about it?"

"No, I do not. I had a dressmaking shop in town and I didn't know until I came home that she had signed it."

"Did you by any chance retain over the years any of the copies of the newspapers that carried the accounts of the trials or his release or anything of that nature?"

"No, I only have the account of the death of my father."

"When he [Williams] was released from prison, did the papers here make any comment on it? Did they carry any articles on his being released or was an acknowledgment made of it?"

"Yes, there was. The editorial I've seen. I know there was a beautiful editorial when the picture came here, when they had that premiere here. When that happened I had letters of condolence. You see, my mother was dead then. I had telephone calls — so many people were so indignant. All the old-timers were so indignant for letting it be shown here."

"When the movie came and when they were telling the story of Carbine Williams, of course, they were elaborating more on his inventive genius, but they took in his life and his bad time."

"Oh, they made a hero of him. He served for a crime that he did not commit — that was according to the movie. And the papers full of it, you know. On one whole page was a picture of him."

"To your knowledge, did any of the other Williams boys ever get into any trouble?"

"No, I don't think so. Well, there was one who lived here that was a contractor. I think it was Leon. Doesn't he have a brother that's Leon?"

"Yes. I wondered what he did. I've met Leon, Will, Gordon and Shell, and there's another one who lives in Virginia whom I've never met, the oldest brother. I know he had one who was at the trial. . . .When the movie came here, or before the movie was made, was there any contact made with you regarding it?"

"None whatsoever, but they claim there was. They said they had contacted everybody concerned. You know what I did? I went down to the Prince Charles [hotel] to see him [Marshall Williams]. I was determined to see him and ask him if he didn't kill him, who did. And they wouldn't let me see him."

"You hadn't seen him since the day of that trial until that time, and they refused to let you see him."

"No. His manager, or press manager, said he was tied up with the reporters. He couldn't see me."

"And they knew who you were?"

"Well, yes, I told 'em. And I should have gone up, but I didn't. I talked to the manager."

"That must have unnerved them a little bit."

"I said, 'Well, if he won't see me now he will be sorry when he does.' Because I was determined to see him. As I came home and walked in the house, two plainclothesmen walked in. His [Williams'] manager had warned him and told him that I had threatened his life. And they wanted them to stay here and watch me. That was embarrassing."

"Well now, did they stay here?"

"No, they found out who it was and they were so mad. They said, 'Why Mrs. Stevens!' It was Mr. Monroe and Mr. (I forgot his name). I knew them both. In the meantime, the chief called me and told me that he had just found out that it was me that they were coming to see, and if he could get up with them [the plainclothesmen] before they got here, he'd call them off. But if he couldn't, to please forgive him because he knew that it would be embarrassing. Well, the funny part was I went against my husband's will. He didn't know I was going. I didn't tell him."

"I can see that you've got some of the sheriff's determination in you. Well, during Carbine Williams' stay here in Fayetteville for this parade, did you ever see him or have you ever talked to him?"

"No, never did. Well, I met him on a street I was driving down, and there was this big, black Cadillac with 'Carbine Williams' in gold on the side. It was on the side of his Cadillac, 'Carbine Williams.' Oh, and another thing, when they had the picture here, this old John (a colored man that I didn't even know was living) who loved my father so, came to see me. I heard someone rap at the steps in the back and I went out and he said, 'I'm old John. Don't you remember me? You know, if you want me to do it, old John can just shoot him and nobody will never know who done it. If you want me to do it, I'll do it,' he said."

"This was an old colored man who really loved your father."

"He loved my father. I said, 'No, John, there has been too much trouble already. Don't do anything like that.' That's what he wanted to do. He had ideas of going down in the parade, you know, and when he [Williams] paraded by, he was gonna shoot him."

"Have you or your family ever been to the movie *Carbine Williams*?"

"My family and my husband went to the drive-in after it was premiered here."

"And you say your sisters were indignant about this?"

"They were. They didn't want me to go but I went anyway. I was determined to see just what it was. That's when I called Ridenhour and told him it was the biggest lie I had ever seen on the screen. There wasn't one bit of truth about it. Not one bit."

"Well, what was his response about it when you told him, Ridenhour being the publicity man?"

"Oh, as far as he was concerned, 'It was all the truth.' That was his reply. It made him mad. I didn't care much about it."

"I was in Carbine's shop one day and, during interviews, found that he contributed an enormous amount of money to the Sheriffs Association when they founded the Deputy Sheriffs League. I think this was, in his own way, one way of trying to reconcile his act."

"He had the portrait [painted] of Sheriff McGeachy. He presented that, I believe, to the courthouse."

"Now, at the time of the funeral, you say that next door there was no house built?"

"Yes, next door here was a vacant lot."

"And all the colored people of the community stood over there?"

"Well, there were hundreds of them. Dr. Snyder stood on the porch and made his speech. My father walked right out on these steps the last time. After my mother died, when I opened the big Bible to record something, I found a flower in there that she had told me about years before. When he went out, he said, 'Mother, this is a beautiful flower.' He put his hand on it, you know. It was a geranium. She pressed it in the Bible and we didn't know it until after her death."

Epilogue

As age began to take its toll on Marshall Williams, close friends and acquaintances began to worry that unless some plan were made to preserve and protect his tools and historic weapons, they might be lost. No one had any idea that Marshall Williams was also mindful of this and was giving considerable thought and concern to it. Williams had for years graciously received hundreds of school children bused out to the Williams farm to meet him and to visit his famous shop. He wanted to make arrangements that would permit not only these students but all interested persons to continue to visit his shop long after he was gone.

At a point during this period of concern, a reunion was held at historic Old Bluff Presbyterian Church and Governor Robert Scott of North Carolina was the speaker. As the Williamses were leaving the church, Marshall saw Governor Scott walking across the churchyard. "Gordon, I want to have a talk with Governor Scott. Run over there and see if you can arrange this for me," Marshall requested. (Carbine was a close friend of Governor Scott's father.) Gordon arranged for his brother to talk with the governor although he was totally unaware of the nature of the conversation. As Marshall walked quietly through the church yard with the governor, he asked him if he or the state would have any interest in moving, preserving and displaying his shop and all inventor's models. Governor Scott expressed great interest and delight, whereupon Williams agreed to give his shop, tools and all weapons and related items to the State of North Carolina.

According to Gordon Williams, Carbine walked back over to him and simply said, "Gordon my talk was successful." Nothing more was said and still Gordon did not know what Carbine and the governor had discussed. But several days later, Marshall Williams asked Gordon to come into the shop and explained in detail what he had done and said: "Gordon, I'd like your approval and blessings in this."

Governor Scott wasted no time. On return to his offices he immediately activated several state agencies that were to be deeply involved in this project.

North Carolina has an unusually strong, effective and well organized Department of Archives and History. During this period Mrs. Joy Jordon was Administrator— North Carolina Museum of History. She is now retired and the department is headed by John Ellington. During the period in which the shop was being prepared for its move, Ellington was Curator of Exhibits.

Numerous highly specialized personnel began making visits to the shop and meeting with the Williams family. Keith Strawn, then Curator of Collections, became immediately involved. Charles Clark had the task of making a photographic inventory of every detail of the shop, inside and outside. These photographs and the use of a grid system later played a key role in the exact reassembly and redisplay of the many hundreds of items in the shop. In charge of the awesome job of reassembly and display was Dennis Walters, Preservationist of the Museum of History.

Needless to say, Carbine Williams was not idle either. Although he was becoming weaker by the day, he once again called on that mysterious inner strength of his and involved himself in the endless activities that were beginning to take place. He saw to it that no detail was overlooked, including a pack of his Camel cigarettes, left in the shop as he so often did while working there. He saw to it that those involved understood what each item was, where it came from and what it meant in relation to his life and inventions. He was invaluable in this for he alone knew these details. Although he was ill, it was debatable as to who was tiring out whom, for on numerous occasions these specialists left the Williams farm quite exhausted from the continuous pace of the day set by Marshall Williams.

The North Carolina Highway Department was also much involved in the relocation of the shop. There was the painstaking job of disassembly, since the Archives Building had no exterior doors through which it could pass, and then the task of carefully moving this building to Raleigh. The relocation was accomplished by many capable people and was headed by C. L. Young.

In recalling preparations following the move, Administrator John Ellington said, "When we had finalized our work, Carbine came and personally inspected every detail of our finished product to be sure that it was exactly as it was when the shop was located on his farm near Godwin, North Carolina. In my opinion, Carbine's shop and related items is by far the most popular exhibit in the museum and certainly maintains a high visit level. Further, it is the exhibit most commented on."

Once, while discussing the fact that someday his shop would be moved and preserved at the State Archives Building, Williams attempted to conceal his concern about his beloved shop's leaving Godwin: "Ross when we get the ol' shop on that truck," Marsh joked, "you and I will hang out the back door, yell and fire a few rounds just for the hell of it. Won't that be somethin'?"

Miss Maggie knew best of all how the move, once it was accomplished, really affected Williams. "Ross," she confided, "with the shop going to Raleigh, Marsh went too. His life went with that shop. I knew it would. We got in one of the brother's cars and rode for a short while behind the shop. We rode just past Godwin, stopped and watched the shop as far as we could see it, and then turned around and came back home. There was no hanging out the door, yelling or shooting. Ross, he just didn't have anything to say. He was mute about everything the rest of the day. You see, his life went with that shop. He was proud to do it and

Photo 44. The June 22, 1971 dedication of the Williams exhibit at the N.C. Department of Archives and History, Raleigh. Left to right: Governor Robert W. Scott, Mrs. Scott, David M. "Carbine" Williams, Mrs. Williams cutting the ribbon. Shortly after this Carbine, sick and fatigued, collapsed. *Photo courtesy N.C. Department of Archives and History*

Photo 45. The interior view of the famous workshop of inventor Carbine Williams. Originally located near Godwin, N.C., the entire shop, as shown, was relocated and is on permanent display at the Department of Archives and History Building, in Raleigh, N.C.

Photo courtesy N.C. Department of Archives and History

Photo 46. An interior view of the Carbine Williams wing of the N.C. Department of Archives and History in Raleigh. The photographic history of Williams' life is narrated.
Photo courtesy N.C. Department of Archives and History

proud that his history was being preserved, but it was a traumatic moment for him."

The eagerly awaited dedication day arrived on June 21, 1971 (Photos 44, 45, 46). Calling on a final reserve of strength, Carbine attended the ribbon cutting, dinner and dedication. He collapsed briefly before the conclusion but recovered sufficiently to remain for part of the remaining program. A few days after the dedication he entered the hospital. Recovering somewhat, Williams at length was able to return to his home, but things had changed.

"In 1969 and 1970, through both those years, he was too feeble to leave the farm," Miss Maggie recalled. "Very seldom did he go away. He lived mostly in retrospect and reflection. He worried over the way his life was ending and he talked to me freely about it."

"What did he talk about?" I asked.

"Well, he was consumed with a desire to go back home" [the original family homeplace], she replied. "I think he felt that he had never been back home, down where we left, and as he got older he could not pass the time any other way. The desire just consumed him. David [Jr.] had come back from California and one day he came by and said, 'Come on Daddy, let's go decide where we're going to put the house,' so he went down and they decided where they would put David's house. Well David went on home and Marsh came back. He did not come in the house then. He went to the end of our porch and looked down there (toward the old homesite where David was now going to build) and he said, 'Things will never be the same'; and, Ross, in four days he didn't know anything. That's when it all ended. I never did tell David that. That was on Thursday and on Sunday he had lost all contact with reality. That's the truth, Ross. . . ."

That Sunday, without warning, Miss Maggie walked in to find Marsh sitting quietly in a chair looking quite distant. Hardening of the arteries had taken its toll. He did not recognize those around him, not even Mrs. Spot, his beloved dog and constant companion. Carbine was mentally far away.

Photo 47. Following a twenty-one gun salute by the U.S. Army at Marshall Williams' funeral, Cecil Edgerton stepped from the sidelines and fired one round from this M-1 carbine in salute to the inventor and in memory of those who had used the M-1 carbine in combat. Here Mrs. Maggie Williams and Carbine's brother Shell join John Williams, along with Edgerton and the president of Campbell College, recipient of the weapon.

Later, Marshall Williams was sent to Dorothea Dix Hospital in Raleigh. His family and friends would visit him regularly and several times he returned home for visits.

On January 8, 1975, David Marshall Williams died. Several hundred relatives, close friends and neighbors gathered on January 10 at the historic Bluff Presbyterian Church in Wade, North Carolina, in final tribute. He was laid to rest in the churchyard, where a simple and touching service was given by Robert Marshall Williams.

While no prominent political leaders attended the funeral, the military was represented, and as Carbine Williams' body was placed at the grave site, an honor guard of Special Forces from Fort Bragg, armed with the new M-16 rifles, fired a twenty-one gun salute. As it was fired, another soldier stood at rigid attention holding the inventor's famous M-1 carbine.

An unexpected tribute followed the twenty-one gun salute. A civilian, Cecil Edgerton, quietly stepped from the crowd, raised to his shoulder an M-1 carbine and fired a single round in salute to the inventor and in memory of those soldiers who fought and survived using his carbine. This weapon was later presented to Campbell College in memory of Carbine Willaims (Photo 47).

Is this the final chapter to this story? I don't think so. True, Carbine Williams will not invent again, but his weapons continue in use in almost every country in the world. Additionally, in his shop in the North Carolina Archives Building in Raleigh is an invention whose merit has not yet been recognized. Like so many of Williams' ideas, this weapon is twenty years ahead of its time. As our armies fire away at 550 rounds a minute with their latest machine guns, Williams' machine gun has a capability of firing at a cyclic rate of two thousand rounds a minute. It, too, may find its place as today catches up with Williams' tomorrow.

Children who visit Williams' preserved shop will feel the spirit of the inventor's genius; a few will become excited by his story. Perhaps there will be those who receive sufficient inspiration that, upon growing up, they, too, will develop inventions which will contribute to a stronger America. Hopefully, in their lifetime, they will receive more recognition and appreciation from their country.

Photo 2-44a "Carbine" Williams holds a strip of steel that he used to test the bullet penetration of his guns. Making guns wasn't nearly enough, they had to shoot hard and accurate (R.E. Beard).

Appendices

Examples of Some of the Weapons
Invented and Built by Williams

Patent Nos.	Inventions	Dates of Issue
2,027,892	Gun	Jan. 14, 1936
2,027,893	Belt Feeding Means for Guns	Jan. 14, 1936
2,090,656	Automatic Firearm	Aug. 24, 1937
2,090,657	Automatic Firearm	Aug. 24, 1937
2,144,951	Firearm	Jan. 24, 1939
2,174,851	Safety Mechanism for Firearms	Oct. 3, 1939
2,204,289	Extractor Mechanism for Firearms	June 11, 1940
2,242,496	Sear Mechanism for Firearms	May 20, 1941
2,286,133	Firearm	June 9, 1942
2,289,158	Firearm	July 7, 1942
2,308,257	Automatic Firearm Construction	Jan. 12, 1943
2,323,954	Front Band Construction for Firearm	July 13, 1943
2,325,646	Receiver & Trigger Construction for Firearm	Aug. 3, 1943
2,334,300	Pivotal Rear Sight for Firearm	Nov. 16, 1943
2,336,146	Firearm	Dec. 7, 1943
2,336,431	Takedown Firearm	Dec. 7, 1943
2,341,005	Piston Means for Gas-Operated Firearms	Feb. 8, 1944

2,341,680	Piston Means for Gas-Operated Firearms	Feb. 15, 1944
2,345,083	Takedown Firearm	March 28, 1944
2,346,954	Gas-Operated Self-Loading Firearm	Apr. 18, 1944
2,348,872	Gas-Operated Automatic Firearm	May 16, 1944
2,350,484	Firearm With Sling Strap	June 6, 1944
2,353,800	Firearm Construction	July 18, 1944
2,355,768	Gas-Operated Self-Loading Firearm	Aug. 15, 1944
2,355,769	Cartridge-Deflecting Means for Repeating Firearms	Aug. 15, 1944
2,361,519	Firing Mechanism for Firearms	Oct. 31, 1944
2,366,823	Firing Mechanism for Firearms	Jan. 9, 1945
2,373,213	Receiver-Assembly for Firearms	Apr. 10, 1945
2,373,622	Firearm	Apr. 10, 1945
2,376,466	Piston Means for Gas-Operated Firearms	May 22, 1945
2,377,737	Firearm	June 5, 1945
2,404,555	Bolt Action Firearm	July 23, 1946
2,412,663	Cartridge-Extracting Mechanism for Firearms	Dec. 17, 1946
2,461,670	Automatic Sear Releasing Mechanism for Firearms	Feb. 15, 1949
2,476,232	Inertia Operated Bolt Lock	July 12, 1949
2,494,220	Ejector Pin and Breechlock Assembly for Firearms	Jan. 10, 1950
2,506,982	Carrier Spring for Magazine-Type Firearms	May 9, 1950
2,509,382	Cartridge-Feeding Mechanism for Firearms	May 30, 1950
2,600,176	Unitary Hammer-Spring and Trigger-Primer for Firearms	June 10, 1952
2,679,123	Takedown Mechanism for Firearms	May 25, 1954
2,847,787	Firearm with Movable Chamber and Sealing Sleeve	Aug. 19, 1958

GENERAL ASSEMBLY
OF NORTH CAROLINA
1971 SESSION
RATIFIED BILL

RESOLUTION 20
SENATE JOINT RESOLUTION 215

A JOINT RESOLUTION HONORING
DAVID MARSHALL "CARBINE"
WILLIAMS.

Whereas, David Marshall "Carbine" Williams was born on November 13, 1900, near Godwin, North Carolina, a son of the late James Claude and Laura Williams; and

Whereas, while as a young man confined to prison in the 1920's, by working with hand tools and crude equipment, Mr. Williams invented the Williams floating chamber and short stroke piston concept which revolutionized the design and manufacture of firearms; and

Whereas, Mr. Williams has since that time patented dozens of inventions resulting in improved firepower, several of which contributed greatly to the success of the United States Armed Forces during World War II; and

Whereas, Mr. Williams' fame as an expert on guns became worldwide and resulted in favorable publicity to himself and to the State of North Carolina; and

Whereas, during the nearly 42 years since his pardon from a prison sentence, Mr. Williams has practiced exemplary citizenship and has demonstrated an attitude of compassion which qualities have won for him the respect of his fellow citizens in his home county of Cumberland and throughout the country, a respect that has led to the bestowal upon him of many honors, including a motion picture of his life and many feature articles, which reflected the strength of his faith and spirit; and

Whereas, Mr. Williams has, through the testimony of his life, demonstrated to his fellow citizens that adversity in youth need not hinder the development of good citizenship; and

Whereas, Mr. Williams on this date honors the General Assembly of North Carolina by his presence in the galleries; Now, therefore, be it resolved by the Senate, the House of Representatives concurring:

Section 1. On behalf of the citizens of North Carolina, the General Assembly congratulates David Marshall "Carbine" Williams for overcoming misfortunes which might have broken weaker men and expresses its appreciation for his contributions to the State and nation not only through his inventive genius but also through his citizenship as a North Carolinian and an American.

Sec. 2 The General Assembly further expresses to Mr. Williams and his wife, Mrs. Margaret Cook Williams, affectionately known as "Miss Maggie," its best wishes for many more happy years.

Sec. 3. This resolution shall become effective upon its ratification.

In the General Assembly read three times and ratified, this the 5th day of March 1971.

H. P. Taylor, Jr.
President of the Senate

Philip P. Godwin
Speaker of the House of Representatives

SUMMARY OF COURT RECORDS OF THE TRIAL AND CONVICTION OF DAVID MARSHALL WILLIAMS

COURT TRIAL RECORDS, CRIMINAL TERM AUGUST, 1921 THE CUMBERLAND COUNTY COURT, NORTH CAROLINA

STATE VS. MARSHALL WILLIAMS— MURDER

The Grand Jury being duly constituted and polled returned the following true bill:

STATE OF NORTH CAROLINA CUMBERLAND COUNTY

SUPERIOR COURT AUGUST TERM, 1921

The jurors for the State upon their oath present that Marshall Williams, late of the County of Cumberland, on the 22nd day of July, in the year of our Lord one thousand nine hundred and twenty-one, with force and arms, at and in the county aforesaid, feloniously, willfully, and with malice of forethought, did kill and murder A. J. Pate against the form of the statute in such case made and provided, and against the peace and dignity of this State.

McLean, Solicitor
S. B. McLean, Solicitor
9th Judicial District

STATE VS. MARSHALL WILLIAMS— MURDER

Pros. Witnesses: Henry Dawson, C. M. Yarborough, G. H. Starling, Mrs. Catherine McPhail, Bob Godwin, G. S. Honeycutt, N. A. Godwin, Frank Smith, Aubrey Godwin, W. P. West, George West, C. H. Randall, Chas. Driver, M. C. McLean, N. H. McGeachy.

Found a true bill.

G. C. Trice
Foreman, Grand Jury

STATE VS. MARSHALL WILLIAMS— MURDER

The prisoner having been formally arraigned, the counsel for him says he is insane and cannot answer the charge preferred against him. The court then orders the issue of his insanity to be tried at the next criminal term to be held for this county, regular or special, and the case is continued until then.

John H. Kerr
Judge Presiding

OCTOBER SPECIAL CRIMINAL TERM
1921
STATE VS. MARSHALL WILLIAMS— MURDER

The following good and lawful men are sworn and impaneled to try the issues joined between the State and the defendant to wit: W. G. Leonard, F. R. Cook, W. C. Allen, W. E. Bedsole, A. C. Willis, T. J. Starling, C. J. Smith, A. D. Mason, W. E. Jackson, Willie Smith, G. R. Horne, and J. G. Springs.

The defendant Marshall Williams, having been formally arraigned as provided by law, his counsel say for him that he is now insane and cannot answer the charge of murder as preferred in the bill and request that the issue of his sanity be now submitted to the jury.

And the issue is thereupon submitted to the above named jury.

Tuesday, October 11, 1921

John H. Kerr
Judge Presiding

The trial then proceeds through Tuesday, October 11, 1921; Wednesday, October 12; Thursday, October 13; and Friday, October 14, until 11:15 o'clock p.m. Then Saturday, October 15, until 11:00 p.m., at which hour the case is in the hands of the jury and no verdict has been returned. Reconvenes at 9:30 o'clock a.m. Sunday, October 16, there still being no verdict at 11:00 p.m. Sunday, October 16, recess is taken until 9:30 a.m. on Monday, October 17. At that hour trial recommenced. At 10 o'clock a.m. Monday, October 17, 1921, the jury being still unable to agree upon a verdict, a juror is withdrawn and a mistrial ordered. The court then adjourns.

John H. Kerr
Judge Presiding

NOVEMBER CRIMINAL TERM 1921
TUESDAY, NOVEMBER 22

STATE VS. MARSHALL WILLIAMS — MURDER

The defendant comes to court and through his attorney withdraws the plea of insanity heretofore entered in the case. The attorneys for the defense being as follows: Shaw & Shaw, Nimocks & Nimocks, Clifford & Townsend, and Bullard & Stringfield.

The attorneys for the defendant, Marshall Williams, by agreement with the counsel for the

State and the solicitor, enter a plea of "not guilty" of murder in the first degree and enter a plea of "guilty" of murder in the second degree, which plea is accepted by the court upon recommendation of the counsel for the State and the solicitor. The attorneys representing the defendant at this term being the same attorneys who represented him in the former term in which the plea of insanity was entered.

There was then called for trial the case involving Williams and others on the charge of making liquor.

THE STATE VS. MARSHALL WILLIAMS, BOB GODWIN, AUBREY GODWIN, R. A. DAWSON, FRANK SMITH AND N. A. GODWIN—MAKING LIQUOR

The defendant, Marshall Williams, comes into court and through his attorneys enters a plea of "guilty." Judgement suspended.

Henry P. Lane
Judge Presiding

STATE VS. MARSHALL WILLIAMS— MURDER
FRIDAY, NOVEMBER 25, 1921

Judgment of the court is that defendant, Marshall Williams, be confined in the State Prison for a term of thirty (30) years at hard labor, to wear a felon's stripes.

Henry P. Lane
Judge Presiding

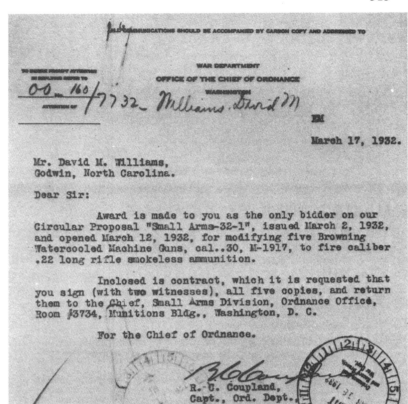

WAR DEPARTMENT

OFFICE OF THE CHIEF OF ORDNANCE

WASHINGTON

O-O No. 160/77732 Williams, David M

March 17, 1932.

Mr. David M. Williams,
Godwin, North Carolina.

Dear Sir:

Award is made to you as the only bidder on our
Circular Proposal "Small Arms-32-1", issued March 2, 1932,
and opened March 12, 1932, for modifying five Browning
Watercooled Machine Guns, cal..30, M-1917, to fire caliber
.22 long rifle smokeless ammunition.

Inclosed is contract, which it is requested that
you sign (with two witnesses), all five copies, and return
them to the Chief, Small Arms Division, Ordnance Office,
Room #3734, Munitions Bldg., Washington, D. C.

For the Chief of Ordnance.

R. C. Coupland,
Capt., Ord. Dept.,
Assistant.

Incl.
Contract (5 copies).

The following three documents relate to Williams' first government contract: modification of the Browning Watercooled
Machine Gun, .30 caliber M-1917, to fire .22 long rifle ammunition. He put in a bid on March 12, 1932 and was awarded the
contract on March 17. Williams penned on the bid schedule,
"No other one or company made a Bid as they did not know
how to get great operating energy from a small calibre cartridge—
my Floating Chamber was the answer. . . ."

STANDARD GOVERNMENT FORM OF BID

(SUPPLY CONTRACT)

Proposal:
Small Arms-32-1.
3/2/32.

ORIGINAL
DUPLICATE
TRIPLICATE
Indicate which by erasure

Opening Date for this Bid

11 A. M., March 12, 1932

To Small Arms Division, Ordnance Office, PLACE *Godwin N.C.*
War Department, Room #5735,
Munitions Bldg., Washington, D. C. DATE *March 5 1932*

In compliance with your invitation for bids to furnish materials and supplies listed on the reverse hereof or on the accompanying schedules, numbered:

the undersigned, *David M. Williams*

a corporation organized and existing under the laws of the State of
a partnership consisting of

an individual trading as *David M. Williams.*
of the city of *Godwin. North Carolina*
hereby proposes to furnish, within the time specified, the materials and supplies at the prices stated opposite the respective items listed on the Schedules and agrees upon receipt of written notice of the

acceptance of this bid within _____ days (60 days if no shorter period be specified) after the date of opening of the bids, to execute, if required, the Standard Government Form of Contract (Standard Form No. 32) in accordance with the bid as accepted, and to give bond, if required, with good and sufficient surety or sureties, for the faithful performance of the contract, within 10 days after the prescribed forms are presented for signature.

Discount will be allowed for prompt payment as follows: 10 calendar days _____ per cent; 20

calendar days _____ per cent; 30 calendar days _____ per cent; or as stated in the schedules.

(Time will be computed from date of the delivery of the supplies to carrier when final inspection and acceptance are at point of origin, or from date of delivery at destination or port of embarkation when final inspection and acceptance are at those points, or from date correct bill or voucher properly certified by the contractor is received if the latter date is later than the date of delivery.)

Col. E. McKee *David M. Williams*
(Witness to signature) (Full name of bidder)

Godwin

North Carolina.
(Address)

NOTE.—See Standard Government Instructions to Bidders and copy of the Standard Government Form of Contract, Bid Bond, and Performance Bond, which may be obtained upon application.
To insure prompt payment bills should be certified as follows: "I certify that the above bill is correct and just and that payment therefor has not been received."

U. S. GOVERNMENT PRINTING OFFICE 1927   10—1602   (OVER)

SCHEDULE

ITEM No.	ARTICLES OR SERVICES	QUANTITY	UNIT	UNIT PRICE	AMOUNT Dollars	Cents
1	Make the necessary modifications on five (5) Browning Watercooled Machine Guns, caliber .30, model of 1917, to adapt them to operate for full automatic fire, and belt feed, using caliber .22 long rifle cartridges of standard commercial smokeless types.			$500.	$2,500	

The rate of fire of the guns as modified shall be between 400 and 480 rounds per minute.

Each gun will be required to fire one thousand (1000) rounds as an acceptance test. There must be no breakages of major parts and not over five per cent (5%) of malfunctions with any gun.

The contractor will furnish with each gun two 100-round belts adapted for caliber .22 ammunition.

The United States will furnish contractor, free of charge, five (5) Browning Watercooled Machine Guns, caliber .30, model of 1917, together with such additional spare parts as may be necessary for the purpose of modification; also ten (10) caliber .22 gun barrels. Title to all this property shall remain with the United States.

The United States will also furnish for use in testing these guns ten thousand (10,000) rounds of caliber .22 long rifle ammunition.

Delivery shall be made within five months.

Payment will be made upon delivery and acceptance of the completed modified guns.

It is hereby certified that in the event award is made to the undersigned, the articles or materials furnished the United States will be of the growth, production, or manufacture of the United States, except as noted below or otherwise indicated in this bid.

[handwritten marginal note, vertical:] I removed a stiffer pin above trigger →

[handwritten:] no other one or company made a Bid as they did not know how to get great operating energy from a small Calibre Cartridge — my Floating Chamber was the answer — It is

(Continued on _____ sheets of Standard Form 36, attached hereto, each of which should bear the name of the bidder)

NOTE.—Insert in this schedule conditions of delivery.

[handwritten:] the only known way of getting great operating energy from a small Cartridge at this time

Photo 2-38a Carbine holds the first gun he ever whittled. A
black powder single shot that works to this day!
(R.E. Beard).

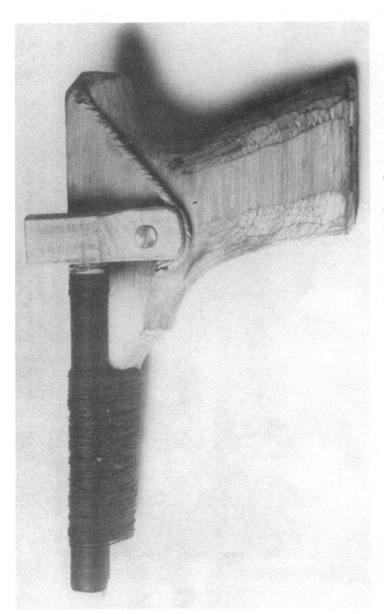

Photo 2-36a   Close-up of the pistol that David Williams first carved (R.E. Beard).

Photo 2-3a Carbine Williams poses next to a statue of young Sam Colt, who supposedly whittled the design for his first gun. Carbine does some gun whittling himself (R.E. Beard).

Photo 1-18   REB, the author, and "Carbine" Williams enjoy an afternoon of shooting at Williams' farm (R.E. Beard).

Photo 1-3   A shop photo showing the lathe that Williams used to build his later innovative designs (R.E. Beard).

Photo 1-29   Carbine's brother Shell works on a unique machine gun design (R.E. Beard).

Photo 1-36   The author, Ross E. Beard, holds the chamber and barrel of the new Williams' machine gun design.